Arthur Harry Church

The Anatomy of Flowers

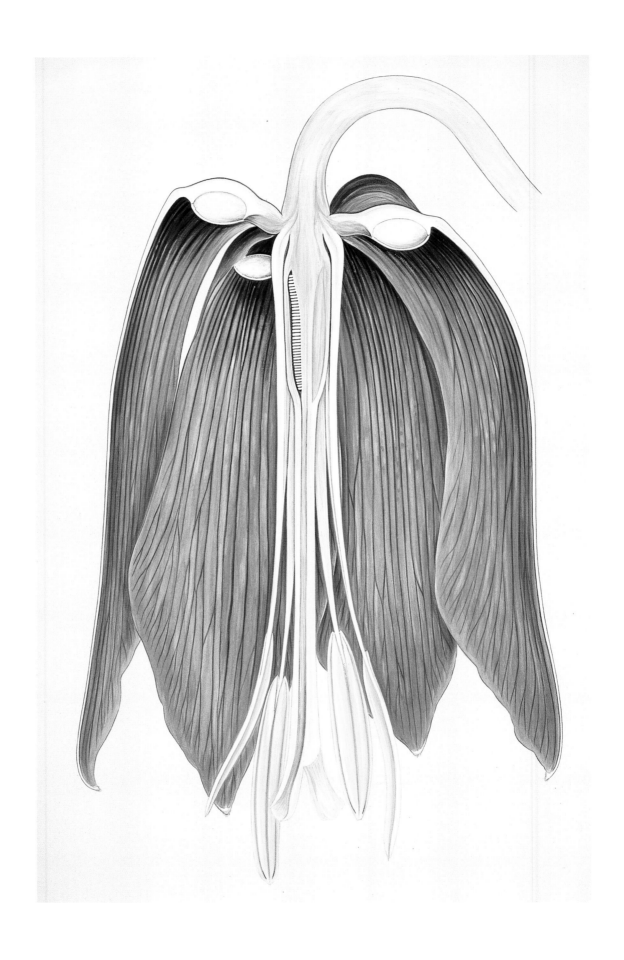

Arthur Harry Church

The Anatomy of Flowers

DAVID MABBERLEY

MERRELL

and

THE NATURAL HISTORY MUSEUM, LONDON

Unless otherwise stated, all photographs are taken from the book
and portrait collections of The Natural History Museum, London.

The Natural History Museum would like to thank the Charles Hayward Foundation
for supporting the publication of this book.

First published in 2000 by
Merrell Publishers Limited
42 Southwark Street, London SE1 1UN
and
The Natural History Museum, London

Distributed in the USA and Canada by Rizzoli International Publications, Inc.
through St Martin's Press, 175 Fifth Avenue, New York, New York 10010

British Library Cataloguing-in-Publication Data
Mabberley, David
Arthur Harry Church : the anatomy of flowers
1.Church, A. H. (Arthur Harry), 1865–1937
2.Botanical illustration
I.Title II.Natural History Museum (London, England)
743.9'34

ISBN 1 85894 116 4

Designed by Roger Davies
Layout by Matthew Hervey
Edited by Matthew Taylor and Julian Honer

Produced by Merrell Publishers Limited
Printed and bound in Italy

Front jacket:
Nasturtium, detail (plate 54)
Back jacket:
Royal blue waterlily, detail (plate 18)
Frontispiece:
Crown imperial *Fritillaria imperialis* L. (Liliaceae), 14 April 1907

Contents

Acknowledgements

Writing this book has been a pleasurable duty, a tribute to the memory of a great botanist. Much has been uncharted territory and I am indebted to many people for help with primary sources, notably my daughter, Laura (University of Exeter), for information on Devon, Ian Salmon (University of Wales, Aberystwyth) on University College, Aberystwyth, Laura Dyer (Archives, Royal Holloway, University of London) on Royal Holloway College, University of London, Simon Bailey (University Archivist), Malcolm Graham (Centre for Oxfordshire Studies), Colin Harris (Modern Papers Reading Room, Bodleian Library), Serena Marner, Anne Sing, Anne-Marie Townsend and Howard Wright (Department of Plant Sciences), Martin Maw (Archivist, Oxford University Press) and Brigid Allen (Archivist, Jesus College) on Oxford, Jonathan Smith (Trinity College Library) on Cambridge graduates, Gerald Boalch (*Botanica Marina*) and Emma Harvey on the Marine Biological Association and Paul Byrne (Raymond & Beverly Sackler Archive Resource) on The Royal Society. Dreena and Roger Higton kindly tracked down Church's grave at Rose Hill; Gina Douglas (Linnean Society of London), Sophie Ducker (Melbourne), Rosie Dunne (National University of Ireland, Galway), Tim Entwisle, Anna Hallett and Alan Millar (Royal Botanic Gardens Sydney), Mark Large (Massey University, New Zealand), Henry Noltie (Royal Botanic Garden Edinburgh) and Timothy Walker (Oxford Botanic Garden) cheerfully replied to queries bibliographical, ecological, nomenclatural and horticultural.

It was a particularly fortunate event when I was contacted by one of the only six living descendants of A.H. Church and discovered that she was living just across Sydney Harbour from my home in Elizabeth Bay: Amanda Aničić has acted as a line of communication with the rest of Church's family, especially Jack Grattan and Kate Fagan, and I am particularly indebted to her for bringing his Scrapbook to Australia for me to study. I am especially grateful to Jack Grattan for permission to reproduce drawings and photographs from it. The staff of The Natural History Museum have provided invaluable support in my getting access to the materials held there: Judith Magee of the Botany Library went far beyond the call of duty in easing my path. Once again, Ivan Katzen, and also Glenn Connell, extended generous hospitality to me when I was working in London. As always, I am fortunate in the support of my family, Andrew, Laura and Marcus, but also my mother, who first recognized my interest in plants by giving me, aged 6, my first botany book (W.J. Stokoe's *British wild flowers*). This volume is dedicated to her.

The Trustees of The Natural History Museum would like to thank the Charles Hayward Foundation for generously supporting the publication of this book.

Introduction

Arthur Harry Church is not a household name, yet his astonishing botanical art is increasingly seen on greetings cards, diaries and posters. It is so striking and original in its genre that it is becoming more and more desirable that something of the life of the artist be put before the public. In 1981 my *Revolutionary botany*, which outlined what was then known of it, was published. Since then much more has come to light and so the opportunity is taken to combine this with an assessment of Church's scientific and artistic contributions.

Church was essentially an academic marooned in Oxford, but his life was full of tragic events and disappointments. From humble beginnings he came to be one of the most knowledgeable, yet one of the least travelled, botanists in Britain. Almost immured in the Department of Botany, then in the Botanic Garden in Oxford, he took solace and pleasure in analysing and drawing the structure of plants, particularly their flowers. But for Church these were not decorative additions to Western culture; they were machines ensuring successful sexual reproduction in plants. By dissection and a study of flowers at different stages of their development, he was able to portray their mechanism in words and brilliant clean-lined, almost *Jugendstil*, illustrations exposing their internal structures. As clinical as the methodology may have been, and as much as he may have considered his drawings a by-product of his science, the freshness and boldness of his style have ensured him an exalted place in the history of biological illustration.

Church's greatest artwork was that for the unfinished *Types of floral mechanism*. Just one of several projected volumes was published – in 1908 – and the bulk of the exquisite watercolour plates he prepared was therefore left unpublished in his lifetime. Most are now in The Natural History Museum and most of those reproduced in this book are published here for the first time. As his great book was to have considered 'the hundred best flowers', largely arranged according to their flowering times, I have presented most of his drawings selected for this book in that way to accompany the text below.

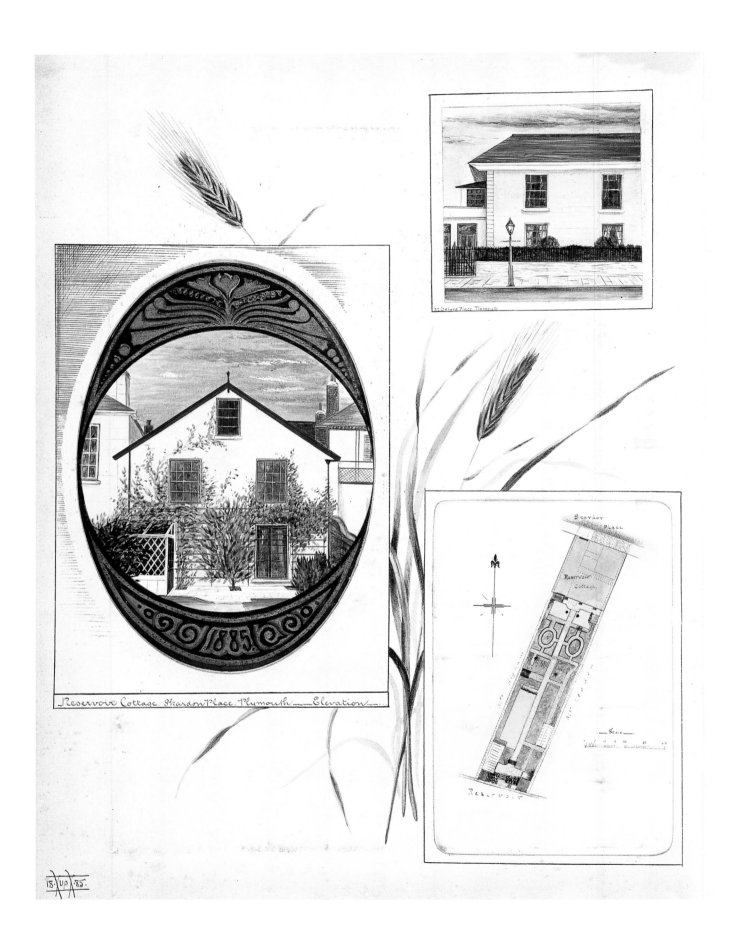

Reservoir Cottage. Skardon Place. Plymouth —— Elevation —

32 Oxford Place Plymouth

Skardon Place

Reservoir Cottage

Reservoir

Scale

8

Devon and Wales

1 Arthur Harry Church, aged 18 (A.H. Church, Scrapbook, f. [1], *recto*; Grattan family).

NOTE: PLATES, FIGURES AND MANUSCRIPT SOURCES

All illustrations reproduced here and all manuscript sources cited are in the collections of The Natural History Museum unless otherwise stated.

The botanical illustrations are by Arthur Harry Church and were prepared in the Botanic Garden at Oxford unless otherwise indicated. Almost all are watercolours of median vertical sections of flowers ('half flowers') on Bristol board, filed according to family in the Church MSS in the museum; where they are not, this is stated. The captions give the current common and/or scientific names, followed by the relevant authority. Family names are also given, in brackets. If Church used a different name, that is given in square brackets or referred to in the caption. Notes to the plates and figures, marked by asterisks *etc.* in the captions, appear on pp. 126–27. The Church MSS in the museum, as also those in the Bodleian Library, are as yet largely unsorted and unfoliated. Any text underlined in the original manuscript sources has been cited here in italics.

PLATE 1 Top: 32 Oxford Place, Plymouth; left and bottom: elevation and plan of Reservoir Cottage, Skardon Place, Plymouth. Watercolour and ink on paper by Arthur Harry Church, 1885 (Church Scrapbook, f. [1], *verso*; Grattan family).

Arthur Harry Church, one of the most original and renowned botanists of his day, had humble origins.[1] He was born on 28 March 1865 at 32 Oxford Place,[2] Plymouth, Devon, the eldest surviving son of a saddlery foreman, Henry Church, baptized in Hereford St Martin's, 2 January 1831, son of William (?baptized 10 May 1806 son of Elizabeth Church) and Margaret Church.[3] His sister Caroline Alice ('Carrie') was by then just two years old.[4] It seems that a son called Henry had died young and so Harry was chosen as Arthur's second name, ensuring that his father's name would be carried on.[5]

His father and his mother, Mary Head Church (née Brown *c.* 1824 at Stoke Damerel, near Plymouth),[6] moved from that little house to Reservoir Cottage, 6 Skardon Place, Tavistock Road, Plymouth,[7] while Arthur was a young boy. According to surviving watercolours by Arthur, it was another small house, sandwiched between two others. It had a narrow garden running down to the reservoir, complete with lawns and formal bedding and apparently two small greenhouses or garden frames.

In 1875 Arthur was sent to Hele and Lanyon's School, Tavistock Road, Plymouth, where he was taught for four years.[8] In 1879 he went on to Cheveley Hall School, Mannamead, Plymouth, and in his two years there took Cambridge local examinations for junior students, in December 1879 and December 1880, achieving second-class honours in the examination which covered compulsory "1. Reading aloud from an English Prose Author. 2. Writing from dictation. 3. Rudiments of English Grammar. 4. Elementary Arithmetic" and five subjects of his choosing: "Religious Knowledge; History, Geography & Shakespeare; French; Mathematics;

2 Plymouth in the 1880s (Church Scrapbook, f. [3], *verso*; Grattan family).

3 Henry Church, 1894 (Grattan family).

4 Mary Head Church (Church Scrapbook, f. [28], *verso*; Grattan family).

Drawing from Flat & Models". In the 1880 examination "he was distinguished" in "History, Geography & Shakespeare".[9]

The headmaster, Daniel Slater, later wrote that Arthur's success was due to his "careful and industrious work".[10] Arthur duly applied to Ashburton Grammar School, twenty-four miles from Plymouth, on the edge of Dartmoor, where he was to study from January 1881 to April 1884. The headmaster, James Mortimer, recalled:

"As I only had one assistant master, I began the practice of taking a boy who wished to be prepared for College, giving him his board and lodging and a very small salary with the assistance in his studies, for half-time teaching. … Church helped me in this way for a long time. Church had been attracted to the School from Plymouth, chiefly because Ashburton was thought to be more bracing. He was not 16, and when he first came to see me it seemed a joke to think of so young a boy as an assistant. I remember taking him into the garden and soon found his eyes had seen far more deeply into the book of nature than mine. His mother had told him to take some of his maps with him, and when I saw them I said, 'All right, I'll take you.' They showed an accuracy of touch, indicating a veracity of character, which will be understood by all who have seen the marvellous illustrations in the books on Botany which have been published for him."[11]

PLATE 2 Ashburton Grammar School. Watercolour and ink on paper by Arthur Harry Church, 1884
(Church Scrapbook, f. [5], *verso*; Grattan family).

GRAMMAR SCHOOL.

ASHBURTON.

FROM THE DOOR.

Arthur H. Church.

.1884.

According to *White's Devonshire directory* of 1850, the school "is kept in *St Lawrence's chapel*, which was given for its use, and as a place of public meetings and the holding of the manor courts in the 36th of Elizabeth. The ancient tower and spire remain, but the body was rebuilt about a century ago", while Ashburton was "picturesquely seated in a fertile valley, to the south, and watered by the *Yeo* rivulet, which runs through and partly under the town, and falls into the river Dart, about a mile below. The *parish* of Ashburton is co-extensive with the *borough*, and comprises … land beautifully diversified with hills and valleys, and generally fertile, though skirted on the west by the lofty hills and barren summits of the Dartmoor Forest."[12]

At Ashburton, Arthur began painting watercolours in earnest, building on the landscapes and maps of his earlier work to produce drawings of plants. He also drew the most detailed maps of the school grounds and copied old ones of the whole town in pen and ink[13] as well as astronomical phenomena such as the great comet of 13 October 1882, the Transit of Venus on 6 December that year and a lunar eclipse of 1884.[14] At this time he seems to have travelled not only in Devon but also to London[15] and, in 1884, to Hull.[16] In that year he began putting his drawings and photographs in a scrapbook. Still in the family, it is all that survives of records of his early life. Soon he was adding to it watercolours made at The Mumbles in Swansea and Land's End.[17] But, decorative as these are, they are the work of a competent schoolboy, nothing more. Many of them are signed with the word 'church' in Greek letters.[18] Drawings and photographs are often surrounded by clouds of butterflies and the photographic portraits with signatures, including one of Sir Joseph Hooker, Director of Kew Gardens.[19] With another pupil teacher, William S. Lambshead,[20] who was a farmer's son from Newton Abbot, he "made a remarkable collection of the flora of South Devon, and showed in innumerable ways a thoroughness, an unwearied patience and a delicacy of finish which are, unfortunately, very rarely met with".[21]

Among his collecting sites were the rocky pools around Plymouth, where he studied seaweeds long before the Marine Laboratory was founded there, "when the water was clean": by 1920 it was "hopelessly dirty".[22]

Although there were two scholarships to Exeter College, Oxford, restricted to boys from the grammar school,[23] Arthur returned to Cheveley Hall for six weeks' private tuition by Slater for the June 1884 London examination. When examined, he was matriculated in the University of London, being placed in the first division.[24] Latterly he was a junior assistant in the school, and Slater wrote of him that

"When during extra pressure of work in consequence of the absence of [the] Second Master he gave me very valuable help. … To any Principal needing a thorough and pains-taking Assistant I can most cordially recommend him. My boys all speak in the highest terms of his teaching which he succeeds in making interesting to them and he maintains good discipline with the greatest of ease."

So early, then, were apparent the hallmarks of a truly inspirational teacher. Arthur was soon taken on again to teach at Ashburton and continued his illustrating, sometimes combining oil and watercolours with tinted photographs.

Now began full-scale watercolours devoted to single plants: one of the earliest surviving studies is that of the corn, or Flanders, poppy *Papaver rhoeas,* of 1886. By May 1887 he was teaching not only at the grammar school, for boys, but also at the high school, for girls.

For lack of funds, Church might not have gone to university but continued as a schoolmaster. But the death of his mother, aged 63, in the long vacation of 1887[25] led to his inheriting £100 and enabled him to go in October to University College of Wales, Aberystwyth, which offered external London degrees.[26] Then, just before he was to leave for Wales, came a second tragedy: the death

PLATE 3 Ashburton. Montage of watercolour and ink drawings by Arthur Harry Church, *c.* 1885 (Church Scrapbook, f. [4], *verso*; Grattan family).

Grammar School. Ashburton. 1884. Arthur H. Church.

5 University College, Aberystwyth. (Church Scrapbook, f. [24], *verso*; Grattan family).

Until the foundation of the University of Wales in 1893, Aberystwyth students read for London degrees. In his first year Arthur took biology, chemistry, physics and mathematics; in his second and third years botany, zoology and chemistry.[31] He was placed in the first division of both the intermediate examination for B.Sc. in 1888, for which he received an exhibition and later a scholarship,[32] and, in 1889, the external London B.Sc. degree. In his final year he lodged at 21 Portland Street with his old school friend William Lambshead. William had passed the London intermediate arts examination before arriving in Aberystwyth and passed his London B.A. in October 1889.[33]

Arthur's teacher for biology was James R. Ainsworth Davis M.A. (1861–1934), lecturer in botany and geology. The course comprised lectures followed by practical work on 'type-forms', mainly drawing specimens.[34] For the elementary lectures on botanical topics the set book was Ainsworth Davis's *The flowering plant* (1890), and one of those for the lectures on zoological subjects was his *Textbook of biology* (1888). Practical work for the advanced courses intended for honours in the London examinations included study of the skeletons in the college's museum: one of Arthur's lab-books, 'Zoology. Drawings, Aberystwyth 1889–1890', survives in the University of Sheffield.[35] Many of the drawings in it are from specimens in the college's museum and some of those of skulls are of a very fine quality, suggesting that Ainsworth Davis or possibly his demonstrator, Samuel A. Moor (died 1944), may well have been a key influence in the evolution of Arthur's artistic style, besides his development as a scientist.

Ainsworth Davis was a Bristolian trained as a schoolmaster at the Royal School of Mines, where (Sir) William Thiselton-Dyer (1843–1928), one of the scientific team under Thomas Henry Huxley (1825–1895), taught botany. The Huxleyan teaching, then alien to the ancient universities, was to sweep all before it in the reform of biological instruction. Ainsworth Davis went on to Trinity

from tuberculosis[27] of his favourite sister, Caroline Alice ('Carrie'), aged 24, on 6 September 1887;[28] this was just some three weeks after the death, at the age of 39, of Margaret, wife of James Mortimer, the headmaster at Ashburton.[29] Although Arthur's father and at least one sister[30] were still alive, these events were a dreadful foretaste of the grief that was to dog him for the rest of his life.

PLATE 4 Plymouth. Montage of tinted photograph and drawings in watercolour and ink mounted on botanical subjects in oil on cardboard, Arthur Harry Church, 1886–87 (Church Scrapbook, f. [19], *verso*; Grattan family).

Breakwater L. H.
Plymouth.

Smeaton
Tower.
Plymouth.

Mt Batten.
Plymouth.

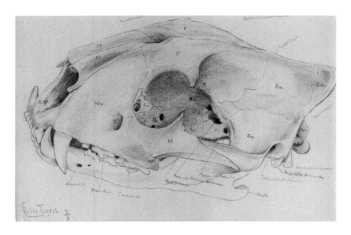

6 Tiger skull *Felis tigris*, College Museum, Aberystwyth. Pencil drawing by Arthur Harry Church, *c.* 1889 (University Library, University of Sheffield, MS 79, reproduced by kind permission of the University Librarian).

College, Cambridge, where he got a double first in natural sciences in 1884.[36] In 1891 he was appointed professor in Aberystwyth and, sporting a fierce waxed moustache, he commanded a company of volunteers in the town at the time of the Boer War.[37] His admiration for Huxley led to his publishing a biography of 'Darwin's bulldog' in 1907.[38]

In a surviving photograph of November 1888 Arthur poses in cap and gown, also sporting a moustache (one he was to keep for the rest of his life), hand on hip with the waistcoat and watch-chain like those of his peers,

looking coolly and confidently at the camera. In January 1889 he poses again, with his hand the same, bowler hat tilted back, swaggering in his good looks.[39] In October that year there arrived at Aberystwyth Emma Palmer Pratt (1868–1916),[40] eldest child of Henry Pratt (born 1840), a pharmaceutical chemist with a shop in the Market Square, Warwick,[41] and allegedly related to the notable botanical author Anne Pratt (1806–1893). Arthur and Emma met and later married, though Emma's antecedents were from the professional and farming classes.[42] She was born on 17 November 1868[43] and baptized at Shipston on Stour, Warwickshire; her brother, Henry Sheldon Pratt, who was to marry a Burmese woman and to be knighted in 1928 for his work in the colonial service, was baptized in Warwick on 28 February 1873. Their paternal grandparents, Henry and Elizabeth (née Sheldon, baptized the second daughter of Thomas Sheldon [1763–1837] on 23 November 1812 at Burmington on the Gloucestershire border),[44] were married at Burmington on 1 August 1837, but their father himself was baptized on 21 April 1840 at Budbrooke, near Warwick, where he married Emma's mother, Sarah Palmer, on 26 September 1865. Sarah was the daughter of John and Ann Palmer, farmers, and was baptized at Budbrooke on 3 May 1841.

Emma Palmer Pratt was educated at Warwick High School and was one of the first twenty-eight students to attend Royal Holloway College, Egham, which had

PLATE 5 Corn poppy *Papaver rhoeas* L. (Papaveraceae). Watercolour by Arthur Harry Church, 20 August 1886 (Church Scrapbook, f. [21], *recto*; Grattan family). The flowers open for just one day and offer only pollen to visitors: bees see the red petals as 'bee-ultra-violet' and the stamens as 'bee-black'; where there is a dark mark at the petal base, bees see that as black with a white margin.* The corn poppy was spread throughout Europe and beyond, to its colonies, with grain crops introduced by neolithic peoples from the eastern Mediterranean. The word poppy comes via the Latin *papaver*, from the Sumerian *pa pa*;† *rhoeas* is a Latinization of the Greek name for the plant, referring to the colour of the flower being like that of the pomegranate. The Greeks dedicated it to Aphrodite, the Romans to Ceres, and it is perhaps the 'flowers of the field' in Isaiah. Before the widespread use of herbicides, it coloured cornfields in summer, but in the English-speaking world it is now most commonly associated with Poppy Day, as it was chosen as the emblem for Remembrance Sunday, commemorating the Armistice in 1918 that ended the First World War, because it had sprung up in the shattered landscape of the bloody battlefields. Shirley poppies, the forms frequently grown in gardens, were selected from wild plants by the Revd William Wilks of Shirley, Surrey *c.* 1880.

7 Anne Pratt (1806–1893), author of *Wild flowers* (1852) and other popular books, was born in Strood, Kent, the third daughter of a prosperous grocer. She lived for a time at Brixton and married, at the age of 60, John Pearless of East Grinstead, Sussex. "She was a bright intelligent little woman, full of interest in natural history subjects, a certain kindness and simplicity of manner, coupled with much gentleness … She was evidently much attached to her husband, whose deafness rendered him a somewhat trying companion."*

8 Emma Palmer Pratt (1868–1916), Warwick, September 1890 (Grattan family).

been opened in 1886 by Queen Victoria.[45] She arrived there in October 1887 but left in 1889 for Aberystwyth without achieving the London matriculation B.A. Arthur graduated B.Sc. London (class 1 botany) at Aberystwyth in October 1890 and then won one of the two scholar-ships offered to mature students by Queen's College and Jesus College, Oxford, in April 1891. Emma, who studied arts subjects, graduated B.A. London (second division) at Aberystwyth in October 1891. That year Arthur moved to Oxford, where he was to spend the rest of his life.

PLATE 6 Snowdrop *Galanthus nivalis* L. [*G. imperati*] (Amaryllidaceae), 1 March 1904. "The three large outer perianth-segments are at once protective and conspicuous; as a rule they do not expand unless the temperature reaches 10°C., and close again below this temperature" (A.H. Church, *Types of floral mechanism* (1908), p. 23). Although *nivalis* refers to snow-white, or growing near snow, the common name is the English translation of the German word *Schneetropfen*, pendants or ear-drops, fashionable in the sixteenth and seventeenth centuries; the generic name is from the Greek *gala-*, milk and *anthos*, flower. Native from Spain to south-west Russia, snowdrops (*G. nivalis*) are widely naturalized in Britain. This form (sometimes called subsp. *imperati*) is a local variant from Italy, notable for its large flowers; the name commemorates Ferrante Imperato (1550–1625), a Neapolitan apothecary .

NOTES

1 Material in this chapter from Mabberley (1981 and in press), unless otherwise stated.

2 Now demolished (Laura Mabberley, private communication, 1999).

3 1881 Census (2194 43 37), Plymouth (Charles), 6 Skardon Place; International Genealogical Index England, Herefordshire.

4 Church Scrapbook, f. [28], *verso*.

5 Grace Grattan to author *in litt.*, 9 March 1978.

6 1881 Census (21943 43 37), Plymouth (Charles), 6 Skardon Place.

7 Church Scrapbook, f. [1], *verso*.

8 Church Scrapbook, f. [2], *verso*.

9 Church Scrapbook, tipped in before f. [3].

10 Testimonial (presented by the late Grace Grattan) by Slater dated 30 July 1884 (private collection).

11 W.S. Graf, *Ashburton Grammar School: the story of six hundred years*, Ashburton (Elson) [1938], p. 19.

12 Posted by B. Randell, 30 January 1999, on http:www.cs.ncl.ac.uk/genuki/DEV/Ashburton/Ashburton1850.htm.

13 Church Scrapbook, ff. [7], *verso*, [8], *recto*.

14 Church Scrapbook, f. [11], *recto*.

15 Church Scrapbook, f. [3], *verso*.

16 Church Scrapbook, f. [8], *verso*.

17 Church Scrapbook, ff. [9], *verso*, [14], [16].

18 Church to Edward Batters, 21 January 1998 (Batters Correspondence, The Natural History Museum)

19 Church Scrapbook, f. [13], *recto*.

20 Archives, University of Wales, Aberystwyth (Ian Salmon *in litt.*, 10 February 2000).

21 W.S. Graf, *Ashburton Grammar School: the story of six hundred years*, Ashburton (Elson) [1938], p. 19.

22 Church to Antony Gepp, 16 December 1920 (Church MSS).

23 *White's Devonshire directory*; see note 12 above.

24 Church Scrapbook, tipped in following f. [2].

25 St Catherine's House Register of Deaths, September 1887 quarter.

26 Archives, University of Wales, Aberystwyth (*teste* Ian Salmon *in litt.*, 1 November 1999).

27 G. Grattan *in litt.*, 9 March 1978.

28 Church Scrapbook, f. [28], *verso*.

29 Church Scrapbook, f. [29], *recto*.

30 Arthur had a younger brother William, aged 10 in 1881, but nothing more is known of him (1881 Census (2194 43 37), Plymouth (Charles), 6 Skardon Place).

31 Archives, University of Wales, Aberystwyth (*teste* Ian Salmon *in litt.*, 20 January 2000).

32 Church Scrapbook; Archives, University of Wales Aberystwyth (Ian Salmon *in litt.*, 1 November 1999).

33 Archives, University of Wales Aberystwyth (Ian Salmon *in litt.*, 10 Febuary 2000).

34 *Calendar of the University College of Wales Aberystwyth 1890–91*, pp. 69–73, 98–101.

35 Mabberley (1981), p. 252.

36 Archives, Trinity College, Cambridge (*teste* Jonathan Smith *in litt.*, 1 Febuary 2000).

37 E.L. Ellis, *The University College of Wales Aberystwyth 1872–1972*, Cardiff (University of Wales Press) 1972, p. 174.

38 *Thomas H. Huxley*, London (Dent) 1907.

39 Church, Scrapbook, ff. [25] *recto*, [26] *recto*.

40 Archives, University of Wales, Aberystwyth (Ian Salmon, *in litt.*, 1 November 1999).

41 Demolished to make way for municipal offices (Grace Grattan, *l.c.*).

42 Pedigree derived from International Genealogical Index England, Warwickshire.

43 Sect. B2, gravestone no. 251, Rose Hill Cemetery, Oxford.

44 Family tree in Grattan family's possession.

45 Royal Holloway Student Register, AR200/1, Archives, Royal Holloway, University of London.

PLATE 7 *Iris reticulata* M. Bieb. (Iridaceae). 19 March 1908. Native to the Caucasus, it is "one of the most beautiful of hardy spring flowers in garden cultivation, and of special interest as presenting in several respects a striking departure from the more usual *Iris* type, and suggesting to a certain extent an approach to the biological habit of the Crocus. … Note … The restriction of the reserve storage to 1 succulent leaf-base, [and] the foot-long leaves, which appear above ground, contemporary with the flowers, belong to lateral shoots which may flower in the succeeding season, i.e. the flower of the main shoot is a delayed formation belonging to the assimilating shoot of a previous season" (Church MSS, *Types of floral mechanism*). The iris flower is effectively three pollination units because of the development "of a tunnel-mechanism by the apposition of petaloid styles over the stamens" (*cf. Lilium martagon*, plate 19). Bees,* attracted to iris flowers by the flag-like 'falls' (and, as in this species, a scent, here of violets), enter the flower for pollen and in so doing deposit pollen from another flower on the stigma, the upper surface of a flap on the outer side of the style; when they leave carrying new pollen, they close the flap, thereby separating the anther from the stigma and preventing self-pollination. *Iris* was the Greek goddess of the rainbow and messenger of the gods; *reticulata* refers to the netted arrangement of the vascular bundles in the dead scale-leaves covering the bulb.

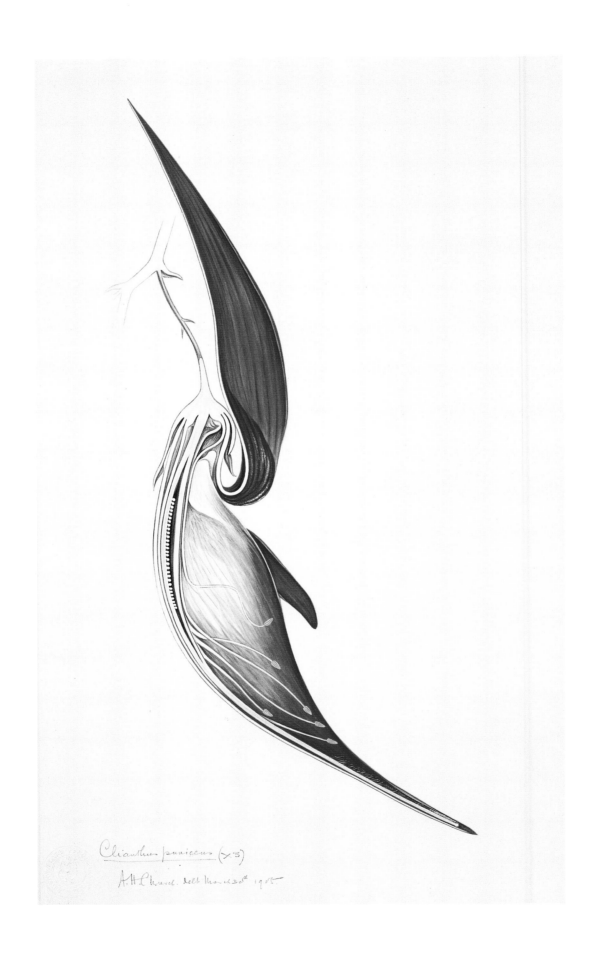

Clianthus puniceus (×3)

A.H.Church. delt March 30th 1905.

Oxford

9 Professor Sydney Vines FRS (1849–1934).
Oil by the Hon. John Collier (1850–1934),
1905 (By permission of the Linnean Society
of London).

PLATE 8 Kaka beak, *Clianthus puniceus* (G. Don f.)
Lindl. (Leguminosae). 30 March 1905. Long
cultivated by the Maori people and perhaps now truly
indigenous in only two areas in Urewawa National
Park, North Island, New Zealand,* this is an
endangered plant in the wild.† But the shrub is
widely cultivated: in 1831 it was introduced to Britain,
where it can be grown outside in sheltered places. It is
bird-pollinated. *Clianthus* is derived from the Greek
kleos, glory, and *anthos*, flower; *puniceus* = scarlet or
crimson, referring to the flowers.

In 1919 Church wrote of the beginning of his Oxford career, "I had really hoped to have done Zoology with [Edward Ray] Lankester [1847–1929, Linacre professor of Zoology from 1891 and fundraiser for the Marine Biological Association's laboratory at Plymouth][1] … the best naturalist with a love of organisms that I ever came across, whatever his faults in other directions. He was a great teacher."[2]

But it was to read botany that Church 'went up' to Jesus College in 1891:

"Freshmen were photographed with the distraction of a shower of lumps of sugar thrown by their seniors. Terms were kept by attending chapel at 8 A.M. or by 'keeping a roller', i.e. putting a mark against one's name on a sheet at 7:40 A.M. in Hall. A short 'choir practice' on Sundays, attended by most men living in college, counted as a 'roller' or chapel if one subsequently went to chapel on Sunday evening. Thus with careful management it was possible to score three out of the [week's] required seven appearances in a single day."[3]

Church was among friends because many Aberystwyth men were there. The college had had a very strong association with Wales from its foundation in 1571. Even by 1882, following the second commission of reform of the universities (1877), half of the twenty-four foundation scholarships plus four additional ones and several exhibitions, were restricted to Welshmen, though education in Wales for the previous three years (often, in practice, at a university college) qualified a candidate of any background. Of the thirty entrants in 1890, the year before Church went to Oxford, five were from University College of Wales, Aberystwyth, four of them with college awards. And, in Church's year, three of the twenty-one entrants came from there, two of them, including Church, holding Welsh foundation scholarships worth £80 a year. And he was not unusual in being a mature student, in that, of the twenty-one in his year, seven had been born between 1865 and 1868.[4] Most were destined to be clergymen, though a famous member there during Church's time was T.E. Lawrence, the Arabist.[5]

PLATE 9 Apple *Malus pumila* Mill. [Pyrus malus] (Rosaceae). 31 March 1907. Wild populations of *M. pumila* in Central Asia are very variable and from this stock have been selected the hundreds of apple cultivars grown today, or their parents. *Malus* is the Latin name for any tree with soft-skinned fruit, such as the apple-tree; *pumila* = dwarf, referring to the form known as 'Paradise apple' ('Malling VIII'), formerly used as a dwarfing rootstock, but now superseded by 'Malling IX' ('M 9'). *Malus* is very close to *Pyrus* (pears)* and should perhaps be reunited with it, though pears have fruits with gritty flesh and purple rather than yellow pollen.

PLATE 10 Broom *Cytisus scoparius* (L.) Link (Leguminosae), 'exploded' flower. 2 April 1903. The flower explodes when a large insect alights on it; "pressure on the wing-petals depresses the keel; the fused line of junction is ruptured … and the enclosed organs fly up with a violent jerk, the pollen rising in a yellow cloud; the hinge dislocates and the mechanism thus acts once only … the style making one complete turn of a spiral either right or left" (Church MSS, *Types of floral mechanism*). But there is more than one chance to be cross-pollinated: in the explosion the short stamens deposit pollen on the undersurface of an insect, the long ones on its back, but they are preceded by the stigma which may contact pollen deposited by a flower visited earlier; the style then grows round so that the stigma is just above the short stamens, ready to catch pollen on the undersurface of a subsequent visiting insect.* Native to Europe and naturalized in North America and Australia, where it is a pestilential weed, broom is used as a sandbinder and for bee-forage. Formerly it was a source of fibre and dyes† and was probably the original *planta-genista* , the source of the Planatagenets' name. *Cytisus* is from the Greek *kytisos*, a word used for several woody legumes; *scoparius* in classical Latin was someone who swept the floor, a reference to the use of the twigs in brooms, hence the English name.

10 Jesus College, Oxford, at the beginning of the twentieth century.

11 The Oxford Botanic Garden. Photograph by Arthur Harry Church, 14 May 1895, reproduced by R.T. Günther, *Oxford gardens* (1912), opposite p. 46. Of the trees, the manna ash *Fraxinus ornus* L., in the foreground, is the only one still alive: it was planted *c.* 1790 (see figs. 21 and 22).

In term time from September 1891 to June 1894 Church occupied Room 8 of Staircase V, a rather miserable, small, second-floor attic room facing east.[6] But he would have spent most of his time at the Botanic Garden, where the Department of Botany was then housed. When Church was working in Oxford, botany – like geology, zoology and astronomy – was a subject largely 'outside' the college system, which was based on fellows who were omniscient tutors preparing their pupils for university examinations;[7] the university recognized the subjects, however, by funding a chair or readership. The professors were supported by departmental or university demonstrators, most of whom never became college fellows.

As admission to the university was – as it still is – through the colleges rather than the departments, there was little leverage to increase undergraduate numbers in such subjects. Moreover, the attractive tripos course initiated at Cambridge in 1881 tended to siphon off science students and Cambridge's funding arrangements were in any case more favourable to science.[8] This distinction between the two ancient universities – 'Cambridge for science, Oxford for arts' – still persists in the popular imagination.

Sydney Vines (1849–1934) had been Sherardian professor of botany since 1888.[9] Early in his career he had helped W.T. Thiselton-Dyer with botanical classes for intending schoolmasters at the Royal School of Mines and consequently later did much to modernize university teaching of botany whilst reader in the department at Cambridge. At Oxford, by contrast, he had less success and it was said that he "put more undergraduates off botany and careers in botany than any other Sherardian professor in history",[10] but the cramped quarters at the Botanic Garden had no facilities for research and his attempts, with the entomologist Edward Poulton (1856–1943) and others, to introduce a tripos-like, less specialized, biology course were thwarted by the university.

In 1896, in which year there were over thirty undergraduates taking elementary practical botany, there were only two doing the advanced course;[11] lectures were given by Percy Groom (1865–1931), one of Vines's Cambridge students. In later years Church was scathing of the teaching he received: "Fortunately I learnt my Botany before I came to Oxford".[12] He attended Lankester's zoology lectures and it was said that Lankester tried to persuade him to take zoology in the final honours school but that "Church was at least as much attached to botany and thought there were better prospects of a University post in that subject, though Lankester's morphological teaching had a lasting influence on him".[13]

Whilst still an undergraduate, Church started publishing original research. In response to a published

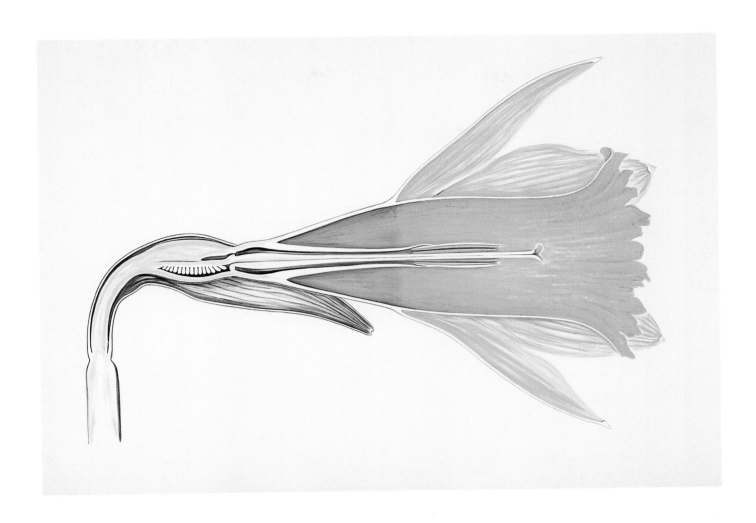

PLATE 11 Daffodil *Narcissus pseudonarcissus* L. (Amaryllidaceae). 3 April 1909. "Indigenous to the whole of South Europe and the Western Mediterranean District, and growing in the open air as far north as Sweden, it also grows in many parts of Great Britain but not in Ireland, in meadows and by the sides of streams, but is very doubtfully native, having in all probability been introduced like other spring flowers (*Crocus*, *Vinca*, Snowdrop) during the Roman occupation. ... *Note* that the biological curvature of the flower-stalk is again corrected in the fruiting condition, so that the open capsule is more or less upright" (A.H. Church, *Types of floral mechanism*, 1908, pp. 118, 126).* It is pollinated by bees. *Narcissus* is a Greek plant name, derived perhaps from *narke*, Greek for numbness or torpor, from its narcotic qualities, or a modification of an old Iranian word. In Greek mythology Narcissus was the youth so enamoured with his own beauty (hence narcissism) that he drowned after plunging into the water after his reflection; the gods thoughtfully turned him into a lily. The specific name *pseudonarcissus*, *i.e.* false narcissus, refers to the fact that the pheasant's-eye *Narcissus poeticus* L., was considered the only 'true' narcissus.†

12 Arthur Harry Church, December 1894 (Grattan family).

assertion that no 'higher' fungus lived in the sea, his first contribution was on a pyrenomycete living on a seaweed, *Ascophyllum nodosum*, which he had seen at Plymouth and also at Bangor in north Wales. His note, already in the literary, yet somewhat tight, style characteristic of most of his later writing, appeared in 1893 in the *Annals of Botany*, edited by Vines, who had been one of its founders.[14]

The next year, the examiners in 'finals' were Harry Marshall Ward (1854–1906), the plant pathologist – another Thiselton-Dyer pupil to whom Vines had demonstrated botany[15] and now professor of botany at the Indian Forestry College at Cooper's Hill – and Francis W. Oliver (1864–1951) – another of Vines's Cambridge pupils, now professor of botany at University College, London.

PLATE 12 Snake's-head iris *Hermodactylus tuberosus* (L.) Mill. [Iris tuberosa] (Iridaceae). 15 April 1906. Found from southern Europe to the Middle East, it is "a curious type of *Iris*, in which the shoot-system perennates wholly below the level of the soil, and consists of a system of succulent shoots, extending horizontally … the unilocular ovary, on which the genus *Hermodactylus* has been based … only represents a retention of an earlier phase of the developmental history common to other species of the *Iris* series, which is here retained in the adult condition, the flower being possibly decadent in its construction, just as the reduction of the shoot to a tuber, the limitation of the inflorescence to a solitary terminal flower, and the frequent loss of an upper spathe-leaf also suggest extreme reduction" (Church MSS, *Types of floral mechanism*). The flowers are scented but are not visited by insects in Britain where fruit is not set. In 1597 John Gerard described the falls as "soft and smooth as is black velvet, the blackness is welted about with green yellow, or as we terme it, a goose turd greene". *Hermodactylus*, a variant of an old Greek word for *Colchicum*, is from Hermes (*i.e.* Mercury), and *daktylos*, a finger.

Iris tuberosa (×3)

A H Church delt April 15th 1916.

Church was awarded first-class honours in botany[16] and Vines promptly appointed him demonstrator.

There were few who specialized in honours botany, though of the handful before the First World War who did, Bertram Bentley (1873–1946), later professor of botany at Sheffield University, got first-class honours in 1896, as did Wilfred Hiley (1886–1961) in 1908.[17] By 1912, when Church himself was an examiner, there were six with honours; the next year, when Albert C. Seward (1863–1941), professor of botany at Cambridge, was examiner with him, there were five, including (Sir) Harry Champion (1891–1979), later professor of forestry at Oxford, of New College, who won first-class honours. There were many Indians in the class lists too.

Church's research work now followed two strands: the study of algae and the study of leaf and floral development. From his next two phycological papers published in the *Annals of Botany*,[18] it becomes clear that he was working in the vacations at the Marine Laboratory in Plymouth,[19] which had opened in 1888, and that he was in correspondence with botanists working overseas as well as in Britain, notably Henry N. Ridley (1855–1956), Director of the Botanic Gardens in Singapore.

On the Plymouth shore Church collected seaweeds, some of them rare,[20] with George Brebner (1856–1905), once a pupil at the Royal College of Science of the palaeobotanist, Dunkinfield Scott (1854–1934) and now

lecturer in botany at University College, Bristol, who was also working at the laboratory.[21] Church later wrote, "Brebner and I used to be the 'algologists' in years gone by [at the laboratory, which had no resident botanists] & I used to preach my view to old Brebner until he used to call me the Plymouth Darwin!"[22] ... He had bad bronchitis, & used to sit for *an hour* at a time in a tide pool."[23] From the laboratory Church sent specimens to the barrister–algologist Edward Batters (1860–1907), and his letters survive in the Batters Correspondence in The Natural History Museum. Church carried out experiments on the seaweeds he brought back to Oxford and illustrated the publications himself. In the long vacation of 1897 he was sending seaweeds from the Plymouth laboratory to The Natural History Museum.[24] The following Christmas vacation he was there again, writing to Batters, "I am hoping to do a set of shore photos to show zones & publish them in the lab Journal", and a few days later he explained that he was thinking of writing a paper on the brown seaweeds of Plymouth Sound.[25]

With increasing financial security, Church married Emma Palmer Pratt at Warwick in the long vacation of 1898.[26] They moved into 21 Warwick [a coincidence?] Street, Iffley Fields, Oxford, a small nineteenth-century terraced house.[27] There in the autumn of 1899 Emma gave birth to a daughter, Audrey Althea (see plate 58),[28] whose second name was derived from the name of the

PLATE 13 Snake's-head *Fritillaria meleagris* L. (Liliaceae). 28 April 1906. Native from southern Europe to the Alps, and first recorded in English gardens in the sixteenth century, the snake's head or fritillary, is now "well-established in the wholly artificial alluvial pastures, and not elsewhere"* along the Thames and its tributaries; it is also naturalized in Scandinavia and the Baltic. It was not recorded as 'wild' in Oxfordshire until 1780† and the celebrated population in Magdalen Meadow, Oxford, not documented until 1785; the seeds are flood-borne. In 1925 Church recorded that "about the first week of April, the general public, especially school children, are affected with a mania for picking the plant as soon as it appears ... and sold by street hawkers (2d. or 3d. for a bunch of a dozen poor blooms), and they are now practically eliminated from all meadows readily accessible to the general public. ... A score of small boys taking some large bunches of buds with little colour, at estimate of 500 per child, will thus denude a couple of acres in an afternoon".‡ By 1933 only two plants could be seen in flower in Iffley Fields, but in 1994 there were 12000:§ by careful management the populations there and in Magdalen Meadow are now maintained, though many other sites have been lost to ploughing and gravel extraction. The flowers are fly- and bee-pollinated but often 'selfed'. *Fritillaria* is from *fritillus,* a dice-box, the chequered pattern of the perianth colouring being reminiscent of decorations on mediaeval dice-boxes; *meleagris* = guinea-fowl, which has plumage mottled in the same way.

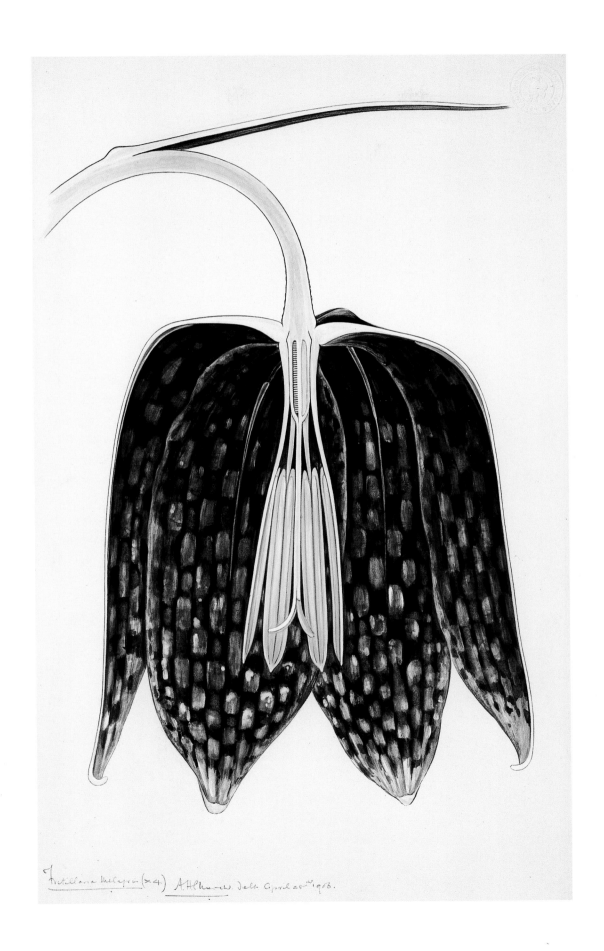

Fritillaria Meleagris (×4) A.H.Church. delt. April 26th 1906.

13 The Botany Department museum and lecture room at the Botanic Garden, Oxford, August 1894. Photograph by Arthur Harry Church, reproduced by R.T. Günther, *Oxford gardens* (1912), opposite p. 64.

the arrangement of the primordia of leaves in buds. Their genesis follows particular spirals and Church began a series of papers he intended for publication in the journals of the Linnean Society of London. They were turned down and he had them published privately by Williams and Norgate, who had an office in Broad Street in Oxford.

On the relation of phyllotaxis to mechanical laws appeared in three parts (1901, 1902, 1904), the first being sold at 3s. 6d., the second at 5s and the third at 5s. In May 1903, Church applied to the Royal Society for a grant to cover the publication costs,[30] but he seems to have been unsuccessful in his bid. It is notable that he referred to himself as 'Lecturer in Natural Science' at Jesus College, and did not mention his departmental position. His short articles on phyllotaxis in *Annals of Botany* in 1901 and 1904 and the first volume (1902) of the *New Phytologist*, founded and published by Arthur Tansley (1871–1955), lecturer at University College London, effectively acted to advertise the book.[31] The volumes, issued in paperback, are illustrated by inked *camera lucida* drawings (see figs. 14 and 38) and photographs that Church took with a plate camera, which is still in the family's possession. The plants, grown at the Botanic Garden, were photographed just outside his window there, "under the sliding window, to the lower frame of which he attached the camera, and this coupling served the coarse adjustment".[32] The third part of the book included 'Mathematical notes' on the spirals: Church was helped by E.H. Hayes of New College in writing these.[33] His interest in the development of these spirals spilled over into studies of floral development and subsequently to his *Types of floral mechanism* (1908).

Church became college lecturer in University College and Exeter College, besides Jesus,[34] and shouldered more and more of the basic botanical teaching in the department. From the start, the Botanical Museum was in his care;[35] by 1904 he was completely overhauling it and build-

hollyhock (*Althaea* [now *Alcea*] was a Latin name then used for the hollyhock), which was in flower when she was born. Just a few weeks later, however, Audrey was dead. In 1902 Emma had a second child, Rosemary Doronica, also given a botanical second name, this time derived from *Doronicum*, leopard's-bane, in flower on her birthday (30 March).[29]

Meanwhile, Church had become increasingly engrossed in the study of the phenomenon of phyllotaxis,

PLATE 14 *Jovellana violacea* (Cav.) G. Don f. [Calceolaria violacea] (Scrophulariaceae). 30 April 1911. A semi-evergreen shrub native to Chile. The six species, found in New Zealand and Chile, of *Jovellana*, commemorating Gaspar Melchor de Jovellanos (1744–1811), a patron of botany living in Peru, differ from *Calceolaria* in having flowers with two corolla lips of about equal size; *violacea* = violet.

(×2).

14 Teasel *Dipsacus fullonum* L. (Dipsacaceae), section taken near the base of a young flowering shoot, 8 April 1901. Original of fig. 64 of *On the relation of phyllotaxis to mechanical laws* (January 1902).

ing up an important collection of economic botany and tropical plant material, particularly from India for study by those going out to the colonial forest service there.[36] In 1907 Groom taught plant pathology and forest botany while the retired colonial servants James S. Gamble (1847–1925), formerly Director of the Forestry School at Dehra Dun, India, and John F. Duthie (1845–1922), formerly Director of the Saharanpur garden in India, lectured to the Indian forest service probationers.[37]

In 1903 or 1904 Church moved with his wife and daughter to 246 Iffley Road, a newly built and much grander house than their first home.[38] In 1904 he successfully supplicated for the degree of D.Sc. in the University of London and in 1907 Emma's third daughter, Grace Coryla, was born. Her second name, like those of her sisters, was a botanical one, being derived from *Corylus*, hazel, the flowers of which were open on her birthday (12 January).

As college lecturer at Jesus from at least 1894,[39] Church taught all of natural science until David L. Chapman

PLATE 15 Green-winged orchid *Orchis morio* L. (Orchidaceae). May 1903. Pollinated mainly by social and solitary bees,* this Eurasian orchid usually dies after flowering. In Greek, *orchis* is a testicle, an allusion to the tubers of certain ground-living orchids. In sixteenth-century botany this orchid was considered a kind of a 'dog testicle' or 'stone', the *kunosorchis*, of Dioscorides, considered important in sex and fertility;† this one was a kind of *cynosorchis morio*, the fool stone. In classical Latin *morio* is an idiot, fool or jester, an allusion here to the perianth segments shaped like a fool's hood or cockscomb. Later it was called *Orchis morio femina* (= female) while the early purple orchid (*Orchis mascula* (L.) L.) was *O. morio mas* (= male) because of its larger tubers or 'stones'. Formerly it was the commonest orchid in Oxfordshire, "but it has been sharply reduced with the destruction of its meadow habitats and is now almost lacking south of Oxford".‡ According to recent DNA studies,§ *O. morio* and its allies appear to belong to the genus *Anacamptis* (from the Greek for 'bent back', referring to the spur of the flower).

(1869–1958), a chemist from Manchester University, was made lecturer. On 19 June 1908, however, Church was elected research fellow for three years, "in order to continue his work on plant morphology".[40] His appointment, perhaps influenced by Poulton, temporarily broke a very 'Welsh' tradition: his two predecessors, both Welsh, were the elderly Revd Daniel Silvan Evans (1818–1903), from 1899, working on Welsh lexicography (he managed to get as far as E),[41] and (Sir) John Morris-Jones (1864–1929), an undergraduate at Jesus from 1883 to 1887, who between 1904 and 1908 compiled an exhaustive grammar of the Welsh language. Church's successor, elected on 24 July 1912, was Richard Ellis (undergraduate at Jesus, 1898–1902), who was to work on the 'Life and Letters' of the Welsh naturalist Edward Lhuyd (1660–1709), keeper of the Ashmolean Museum, Oxford, from 1690 to 1709, but the project was later abandoned.

As the college's sole research fellow from 1908 to 1912, Church was paid £100 a year, in quarterly instalments, to top up his university salary and emoluments as college lecturer at University and Exeter colleges:[42] he was not a member of the governing body and was never to become a fellow of Jesus. In 1908 there were six 'ordinary' fellows, including Chapman, now chemistry fellow, paid £300 a year each, while the Hope professor of entomology, (Sir) Edward B. Poulton,[43] received £200 a year on top of his university salary as a professor (1893–1933).[44] By comparison, undergraduate scholarships, which about a quarter of the freshmen that year had, were worth £80–100 a year.[45] The college was rather exceptional in its fellowship strength in science by comparison with other subjects. Jesus College had its own new purpose-built chemistry laboratory in the block erected along Ship Street between 1905 and 1907, to be used by Chapman until his retirement in 1944,[46] while Poulton, a scholar at Jesus from 1873, had been a lecturer from 1880 and was a distinguished Darwinian.

NOTES

1 *Dictionary of national biography*.
2 Church to Gepp, 9 November 1919 (Church MSS).
3 J.N.L. Baker, *Jesus College, Oxford, 1571–1971*, p. 111.
4 Jesus College Archives (*teste* Dr Brigid Allen *in litt.*, September 1999).
5 See J.E. Mack, *A prince of our disorder: the life of T.E. Lawrence*, Oxford (Oxford University Press) 1996, pp. 56 *et sqq.*
6 Jesus College Archives DO.13–16 (1891–94). The room was substantially modified after a fire in the college kitchen below in 1913 and now has a generous triple sash window. In Church's time there was only a dormer looking out to the battlements (Dr Brigid Allen *in litt.* 6 March 2000).
7 J.B. Morrell, 'The non-medical sciences, 1914–1939', in B. Harrison (ed.), *The history of the University of Oxford* 8, Oxford (Clarendon Press) 1994, pp. 139–63.
8 Howarth (1987).

PLATE 16 Bluebell *Hyacinthoides non-scripta* (L.) Rothm. [Scilla nutans] Hyacinthaceae. 3 May 1903. In May in Oxfordshire woods, "Bluebells are everywhere, scattered thinly, or giving broad patches and seas of vivid blue, with the effect of pools of blue fire, as a colour display not surpassed by any other indigenous or cultivated plant … the maximum [seen] was 320 spikes per sq. yd. flowering simultaneously" (A.H. Church, *Oxford Botanical Memoirs* 14, 1925, pp. 50–51). Native along the Atlantic coastal regions of Europe north to Scotland and typical of ancient woodland, the bluebell readily hybridizes in gardens with the Spanish bluebell, *H. hispanica* (Mill.) Rothm., which is perhaps best considered as its subspecific southern European counterpart. Bluebells are very susceptible to trampling and grazing and cannot survive light levels less than 10%.* "The flowers give a distinctly fragrant scent, and the pollen-supply is sufficient to dust ones boots yellow in walking through them" (Church, *ibid.*). They are pollinated by different species of bee, but honey-bees steal nectar by puncturing the base of the corolla.† The seeds are dispersed by rain, a 'splash-cup' mechanism.‡ The bulbs were formerly a source of starch for linen, and glue for book-binding and attaching arrow-flights. *Hyacinthoides* means "resembling *Hyacinthus*", the hyacinth, a word of non-Indo-European origin and originally the name of a god associated with spring; *non-scripta* = uninscribed, referring to the perianth without markings where that of hyacinth has markings resembling AIAI, "alas" of Apollo, the hyacinth springing from the blood of the dead Hyacinthus.

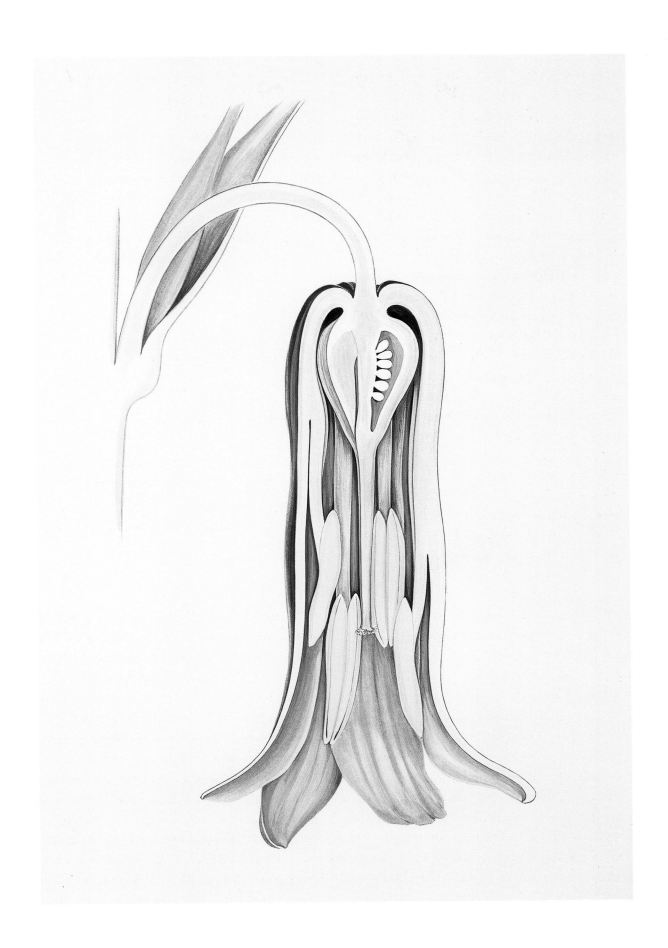

9 T.G.B. Osborn and D.J. Mabberley, 'Sydney Howard Vines', *New dictionary of national biography* (in press).

10 Howarth (1987).

11 *Oxford University Gazette*, 4 May 1897, p. 460.

12 Church to Gepp, 9 November 1919.

13 Tansley (1939).

14 *Annals of Botany*, 7, 1983, pp. 399–400.

15 Bower (1930), p. 54.

16 Oxford University Archives, *Registrum scholarum in scientia naturali, 1864–1924*, UR 3/1/18/1.

17 Oxford University Archives, *Registrum scholarum in scientia naturali, 1864–1924*, UR 3/1/18/1.

18 *Annals of Botany*, 9, 1895, pp. 581–608; 12, 1898, pp. 75–109.

19 According to the MBA records, he visited the laboratory on 17 December 1895; he was on its council 1925–28 (*teste* Emma Harvey *in litt.*, 10 March 2000).

20 Notably *Goniotrichum cervicornis*, March 1897 (*teste* Dr Gerald Boalch *in litt.*, 15 March 2000).

21 Dr Gerald Boalch, *in litt.* 6 March 2000.

22 Church to Gepp, 16 December 1920 (Church MSS).

23 Church to Gepp, 31 August 1919 (Church MSS).

24 Church to Harmer, 21 September 1897, Archives, The Natural History Museum.

25 Church to Batters, 21 January 1898 and 2 February 1898 (Batters Correspondence, The Natural History Museum).

26 St Catherine's House Marriage Register, September 1898 quarter.

27 *Kelly street directory*, 1899–1902. The house is now much modified with unsympathetic additions. In 1897 he was living at nearby 198 Cowley Road (Church to Batters, 11 November 1897, Batters Correspondence, The Natural History Museum).

28 St Catherine's House Births Register, December 1899 quarter, and Deaths Register, March 1900 quarter.

29 Sect. B2, gravestone no. 251, Rose Hill Cemetery, Oxford (R. Higton, *in litt.*, 16 February 2000).

30 Church to Royal Society, 23 February 1904 (Paul Byrne *in litt.* 19 October 1999).

31 *Annals of Botany*, 15, 1901, pp. 481–90; *New Phytologist*, 1, 1902, pp. 49–55; *Annals of Botany*, 18, 1904, pp. 227–43.

32 Corner (1981), p. 5.

33 See Church MSS II 2(a)(vii), Bodleian Library, University of Oxford.

34 *Kelly street directory*, 1904 (Dr Brigid Allen, private communication).

35 *Oxford University Gazette*, 4 May 1897, p. 460.

36 *Oxford University Gazette*, 26 April 1904, p. 512; Mabberley (1995)

37 *Oxford University Gazette*, 30 April 1907, p. 552.

38 Now part of Bravalla Guest House, built as a speculative development by William Rose of nearby Hurst Street (City Engineer's deposited building plan 3556 Old Series (27 June), *teste* Malcolm Graham *in litt.* 12 April 2000).

39 *Kelly street directory*, 1894 (Dr Brigid Allen, private communication).

40 Jesus College Archives, GBM.I, Governing Body Minutes, 1882–1939, p. 243.

41 *Dictionary of national biography*.

42 *Kelly street directory*, 1908 (Dr Brigid Allen, private communication).

43 *Dictionary of national biography*.

44 Jesus College Archives, BU.AC.GEN.25, p. 156, and 26, pp. 152, 167–68 (General Ledgers, 1881–1916).

45 Jesus College Archives, RE.AD. 5–6, Admissions Registers, 1882–1912 and 1912–32, *passim*.

46 *Dictionary of national biography*.

PLATE 17 *Heterotoma lobelioides* Zucc. (Campanulaceae). 3 May 1908. Native to Mexico and Central America and introduced to cultivation in 1861, "in its native habitat it is an alpine form flowering in April and May; in Mexico it is called the 'Little Bird' plant, as the red-and-yellow blossoms borne on slender stalks may convey a distant impression of a group of humming-birds hovering head downwards" (Church MSS, *Types of floral mechanism*). *Heterotoma* in Greek means unequally cut, an allusion to the corolla; *lobelioides* = resembling *Lobelia*, a genus named after the Flemish Matthias de l'Obel (1538–16), physician to James I of England (James VI of Scotland). It differs most markedly from *Lobelia* in that the flowers have crescent-shaped nectar-spurs.

$(\times \frac{1}{2})$

39

(×3.)

AHC. 1907.

'Types of floral mechanism'

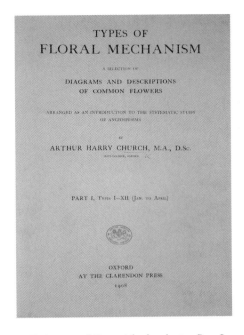

15 Title page of *Types of floral mechanism*, Part I (1908).

PLATE 18 Royal blue waterlily *Nymphaea caerulea* Savigny subsp. *zanzibariensis* (Casp.) S.W.L. Jacobs (Nymphaeaceae), "on the first day of expansion, at 12 noon",* 5 September 1907. Grown in the tank built by Professor Charles Daubeny (1795–1867) at the Oxford Botanic Garden in 1851† for *Victoria amazonica* (the tank survives), this day-flowering waterlily was introduced to Britain from Zanzibar in 1875. Although *N. caerulea* is widespread in tropical Africa , subsp. *zanzibariensis* is restricted to the coastal regions of east and south-east Africa, where it grows in streams and ponds on granite rocks.‡ It has fragrant flowers and is readily raised from seed. *Nymphaea* is from the Greek *nymphe*, a water nymph; *caerulea* means (sky-) blue.

Church lavished enormous care on his lectures and practical classes. He used specimens from the Botanical Museum and Botanic Garden, supplementing them with demonstration material, most of which he assembled himself. For the courses he prepared printed schedules covering the principal points to be made, refining them as his own thought advanced. A visitor wrote of one of his lecture props:

"Church took out from a cupboard the scroll that he used in lectures to convey the aeons of geological time. How long it was I cannot recall, but the present was away along the floor before we had reached the pre-Cambrian. Lecturing, as Munro Fox used to say, is acting. Church was author and actor and composed his own scenery."[1]

For teaching purposes, Church also began a series of floral studies, producing drawings in ink and in water-colour, for class use.[2]

"The subject had to be perfect. He would laugh at the recollection of [E.W.] Hunnybun's drawings for [C.E.] Moss's *Cambridge British Flora* [1914] where beetle-holes in leaves had been faithfully copied, but the mirth carried no sting. Then, the drawing had to be correctly scaled at a magnification sufficient to show the smallest detail that would be required; in the case of flowers he set this at the ovule. The subject was outlined on a sheet of paper; when satisfactory, the outline was transferred to another sheet on which the details were inserted; finally, the pencil drawing was transferred to Bristol board for pen or brush. He used only Bristol board and was careful never to use a firm rubber upon it lest the smooth surface were broken."[3]

Church studied the work of Ferdinand Bauer,[4] particularly the use of Chinese white in the original water-colour drawings Bauer prepared for John Sibthorp's *Flora graeca* preserved in the Department of Botany.[5]

"With ink he used a mapping pen, pushing as well as drawing, and expressed delight if a bit of hair stuck

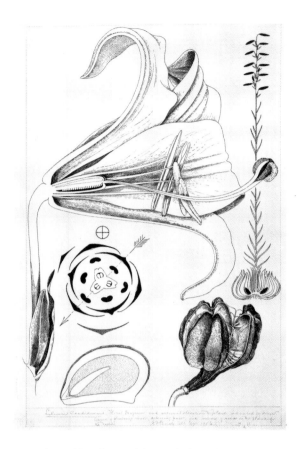

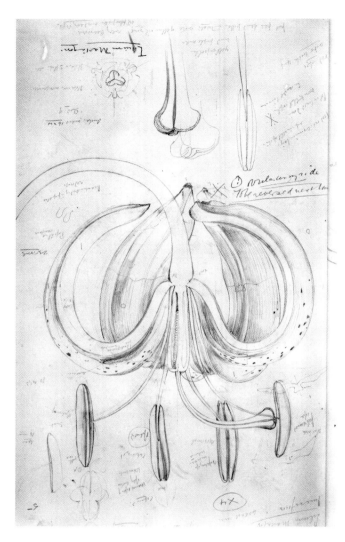

16 Madonna lily *Lilium candidum* L. (Liliaceae). Unpublished figure, ink on Bristol board, 1906. "Floral Diagram and sectional elevation in the plane of zygomorphy. Scheme of bulb and inflorescence-axis. Dehiscing fruit-capsule, and section of seed in the plane of the raphe" (Church MSS, *Types of floral mechanism*). *Lilium* is from the Greek *leirion*, a name Theophrastus used for this lily, but it probably has a non-Indo-European origin, perhaps Coptic; *candidum* = pure white. The Madonna lily is probably native to Israel and Lebanon, but is figured in Cretan frescos 5000 years old and has been cultivated since at least 1500 BC; it has become associated with the Virgin Mary, being figured in many religious pictures of her. The flowers are used in scent-making: 500 kg of them yields 300 g of pure essence.*

17 Martagon lily *Lilium martagon* L. (Liliaceae). Pencil working drawing for finished plate opposite, 26 June 1903 (Church MSS V (v) f. 5, Bodleian Library, University of Oxford).

PLATE 19 Martagon lily *Lilium martagon* L. (Liliaceae), 1 July 1906. The martagon lily, native from continental Europe east to Mongolia and therefore the most widespread of all lily species,* has become naturalized in Britain, the first Oxfordshire record being from Dorchester in 1885.† Each flower acts as a 'multiple pollination unit' like those in irises (see plate 7), in that each of the perianth segments has a tube formed by a furrow at the base and these tubes act as separate narrow entries to the nectar for the tongues of lepidoptera.‡ The word *martagon* is Turkish for a form of turban which this flower resembles.

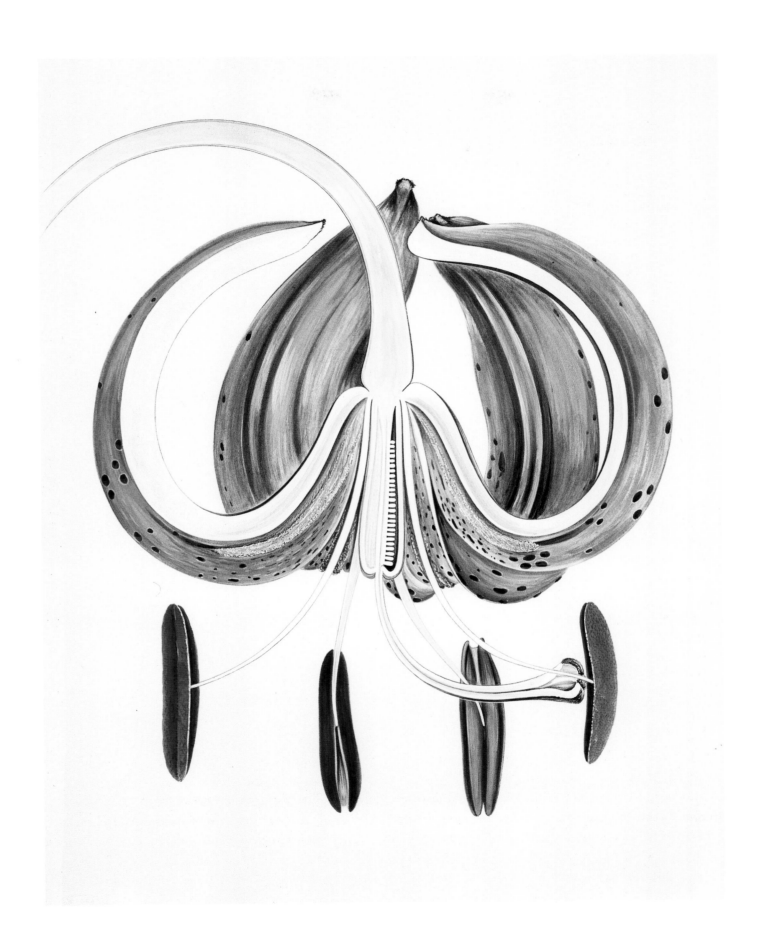

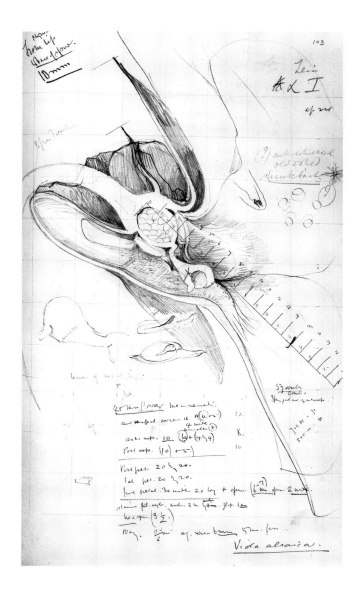

18 Pansy *Viola* x *wittrockiana* Gams ex Kappert [V. altaica]
(Violaceae). Original working sketch in pencil for inked drawing
printed as plate opposite p. 110 of *Types of floral mechanism*, 1908.
(Bodleian Library, University of Oxford, Church MSS V (i) f. 103).
Viola is from the Latin word used for a number of spring flowers,
'viola purpurea' being the sweet violet, *V. odorata* L.; *wittrockiana*
commemorates Veit Brecher Wittrock (1838–1914), a Swedish
botanist who did much to unravel the history of the origin of the
garden pansies. They are hybrids raised *c.* 1830 and involve forms of
V. lutea Huds. from the mountains of central Europe and *V. altaica*
Ker-Gawler from Asia Minor.*

between the points and eased the flow. He drew from
the shoulder and achieved thereby those steady lines
so remarkable in *Types of floral mechanism*. In painting he
used the method of body-colour with Chinese white,
and laid the last tints with an almost dry brush. It
was, so he said, the only way to capture natural
brilliance … with the paints then available this
method required a great delicacy of touch, and it
explains the very slight muddiness that has crept into
some of his pictures. Ovules were modelled as blobs
of Chinese white, then shaved with a razor when dry
for a smooth surface, and lightly tinted. He disliked in
all matters extravagant technique."[6]

These were the materials for *Types of floral mechanism*, a
work that Church intended to publish in several volumes to cover a hundred 'types' of floral structures. He
referred to them as 'The Hundred Best Flowers', perhaps
a joking allusion to the 'hundred flowers' of Chinese art.
They were to be of plants readily grown in English gardens, and each account was to be supplemented with
descriptions of allied taxa. The first part was published
in 1908 and contained twelve 'early spring types'. Church
continued in his Introduction:

"An attempt has been made to strike a mean between
the prosy abstruseness of the academic systematist on

the one hand and the imaginative flights of the enthusiastic adaptationist on the other, and to distinguish carefully what are the facts of observation and what deductions may have been read into them, the more abstract conceptions and ideas, however suggestive they may be, which are not always fully warranted by the facts at one's disposal, are thus relegated to a special end section.

Biological and numerical data, unless otherwise stated, have been collected for specimens grown at Oxford, and represent the result of observations extending in many cases over several years; and the Oxford Garden, being not only the oldest in the country, but also occupying a fairly central position, may well establish its claim to be regarded as a standard for English grown plants."[7]

For each type there is a full description of the plant with scholarly footnotes on origins of the Latin names, ecology and uses, then elaborate descriptions of the flowers themselves and variations of them, discussion of the floral diagram, the development of the flower, the median section, and the actual way the flower works in pollination, discussion of the fruits and seeds, teratologies and then allied taxa, followed by theoretical considerations. The vertical sections were reproduced in colour, the other diagrams as half-tones, each 'type' having between three and five coloured plates. The twelve early spring flower types covered hellebores and winter aconite, snowdrops and snowflakes, jasmines, crocuses, arum lilies and other Araceae, daphnes, violets, daffodils, heaths, flowering currants and gooseberry, japonica and other Rosaceae, periwinkle and other Apocynaceae. Although some of the original pencil sketches survive in the Bodleian Library in Oxford,[8] the original watercolours of the published plates are lost,[9] but slightly different versions, perhaps 'rejects', of some of them, are preserved in The Natural History Museum.

Part I was published on 15 April 1908[10] and went on sale at a guinea: 2000 copies were printed.[11] In July, Alfred Rendle (1865–1938), keeper of botany at what is now The Natural History Museum, reviewed "this very beautiful and elaborate work" in the *Journal of Botany*, noting

"there is nothing else like it. ... The illustrations call for special reference. The full-plate coloured illustrations ... are the best examples of colour-printing applied to this subject that we have seen ... the text is also beautifully printed. But it is all done on the modern highly-glazed paper, the life of which is, we believe, limited to twenty years or so. While it may not be possible to get quite such good results for figures on good rag paper, it is a question whether it is wise to make so heavy a sacrifice from the point of view of durability. The price, 21s. per part, means presumably about eight guineas for the entire work; this is perhaps high from the student's point of view, but is by no means high on the assumption that the standard of production realized in the first part will be maintained throughout."[12]

Church rapidly responded, in a letter to the museum,

"The volume is a purely experimental venture on the part of the Clarendon Press. They gave me a fairly free hand to design it as I liked, but if it does not sell, there will be no more issued (until it does). Even if it does sell, the next part would not be put in the press till next summer; and as the Part issued took exactly two years to print, it will be some time before the series is anything like complete, probably not in my lifetime! So there is no need to suggest that the student has to find 8 guineas! I have had great difficulty in persuading the Press to keep this down to a guinea. I am afraid Part II will have to be 30/- unless there is a great demand for it. ... [I] have been tremendously disappointed with all the figures, both plain & coloured; the methods of reproduction appear lifeless."[13]

And it did not sell. Although "disgusted by the dirty thumb-marks and smudges left by the printers on the originals",[14] Church carried on preparing drawings until 1915 and then, disheartened, stopped. But he did not give up completely. In November 1925 he wrote to the press:

"At any time I shall be glad to hear if the Delegates are ever thinking of doing another volume, Vol II was

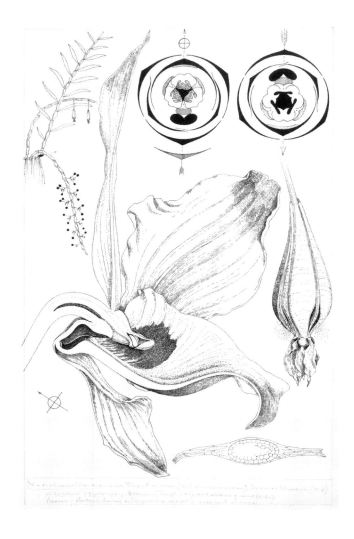

19 *Dendrobium wardianum* Warner (Orchidaceae). Unpublished figure, ink on Bristol board, 1911 (Church MSS, *Types of floral mechanism*). Habit, floral diagrams, median section of flower, dehiscing fruit and section of seed.

finished & all the drawings for Vol III. But as my working time is limited I have no intention (or opportunity) of doing more. The present cost would be near £2000 for one volume: but the first part came out in 1908 & there is still nothing like it in Botanical textbooks. The original plan was for 10 such Volumes: & these would have paid."

But the response was:

"I fear it will be some time before the Delegates could consider going on with the great work. The first Volume is at present £800 on the debit side, without any allowances for interest and to produce a similar volume, with costs as high as they now are, would mean more than double the charge incurred in 1909 [*sic*]. It seems unfortunate that books of this scale and quality are not supported, and if there is any opportunity of proceeding, I shall let you know."[15]

PLATE 20 *Dendrobium wardianum* Warner (Orchidaceae), 10 February 1907. Native to north-east India, Burma and Thailand, this orchid was introduced to cultivation in 1863; it has pseudobulbs up to 120 cm long. Of the 900 or so species of *Dendrobium* (from *dendron* and *bios*, Greek for tree and life, referring to the epiphytic habit) found from tropical Asia to Australia (where there are 71 species) and the Pacific, over 100 are in cultivation in Europe;* *wardianum* commemorates a certain Dr Ward of Southampton.

Dendrobium Wardianum (×4)

A.H.Wood delt. Feb. 10 1907.

Aquilegia vulgaris

1. 2. A. stellata forms.

3. Reduced spur-formation.

Aquilegia vulgaris

1. Cornucopia-form
with 10-striated nectaries.

2. with half the petals
removed. showing elevation.

20 One of the characteristic features of the accounts in *Types of floral mechanism* is the emphasis on teratology, which greatly interested Church (see also plate 21). Mutant forms of columbine *Aquilegia vulgaris* L. (Ranunculaceae). Photographs by A.H. Church; top: "1.2. *A. stellata* forms"; "3. Reduced spur-formation"; bottom: "*Cornucopia* form with 10-striated nectaries"; "2. With half the petals removed, showing elevation". *Aquilegia* comes from *aquila*, eagle, an allusion to the shape of the spurs; *vulgaris* = common. "Double forms again fall into two distinct classes, according to the presence or absence of nectary-spurs; and the combination of various red, purple, violet-blue and white tints with single or double blooms received extended recognition at the time of Lobelius, Dodonaeus and Clusius" (Church MSS, *Types of floral mechanism*).

PLATE 21 *Tulipa* 'Murillo' [*T. Gesneriana*, hort. florepleno, var. 'Murillo'] "showing sectorial segregation in one half bloom to 'Gloria Solis'", 14 February 1914. 'Murillo' was raised *c.* 1860 and among 139 sports of it are most of the modern 'double early' tulips.* *Tulipa* comes from *tulband*, the Turkish for turban, in which the Turks wore the flowers as decoration.

Tulipa Gesneriana, hort.
flore pleno, var. Murillo.
showing sectorial
segregation in one half

bloom to 'Gloria solis'. Oxford. Feb 14/1914.

A. H. Church delt. (×1½.)

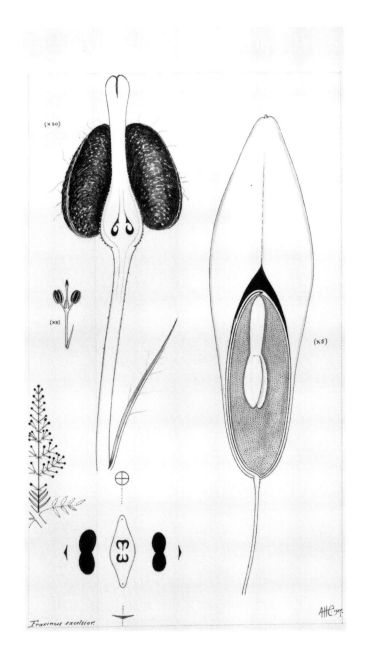

Fraxinus excelsior.

21 Manna ash *Fraxinus ornus* L. (Oleaceae). Unpublished figure for *Types of floral mechanism*, ink and wash on Bristol board, 1907. "Floral diagram and Sectional Elevation in the Median Plane. Elevation of Fruit to correspond, including median section of the Seed in the plane of the raphe" (Church MSS, *Types of floral mechanism*). Native to southern Europe and western Asia, the tree yields manna sugar or syrup which exudes from branches when damaged by insects.* *Fraxinus* was the Latin name for ash; *ornus* was the Romans' name for this particular species. "*F. ornus* can be only regarded as a reduction-specialization of the flower and fruit of *Syringa* and *Ligustrum*, which again are but those of *Jasminum officinale*; while this latter in its construction details has been already put forward as a derivative of the fuller type of *J. revolutum* [= *J. humile* 'Revolutum']. A definite series can be thus traced between an insect-pollinated asymmetrical pentamerous petaloid type and a wholly symmetrically constructed, decussate, apetalous, dioecious, anemophilous tree-form. And this series again can be only read in one way: the phylum undoubtedly presents a steady *down-grade* deterioration of the flower, while retaining a simple generalized inflorescence-scheme; and this is further accompanied by a subsequent morphological deterioration of the fruit-structures, which may also be regarded in the light of reduction-specialization; the 4-seeded capsule of *Syringa*, itself clearly a reduced form of gynoecial construction (cf. the many-ovuled *Forsythia*) becoming a one-seeded indehiscent fruit in *Fraxinus*."

There was not, and it was kept in print until 1955, with remainders appearing on the market for 25s. long after that. Some illustrations were reproduced in popular books such as Lancelot Hogben's *The signs of civilisation* (1959) and Cecil T. Prime's *Lords and ladies* (1960). Thirty years before, in 1928, the *Encyclopaedia britannica* paid 5s. to reproduce part of the plate, the dehiscing fruit of *Viola odorata*.[16] At his death in 1937, Church's papers were left to his daughter Grace, but John Ramsbottom (1885–1974), keeper of botany at The Natural History Museum, offered to take them away. He and George Taylor (1904–1993), assistant keeper, took the beautiful drawings intended for volumes of *Types of floral mechanism*, and selected manuscripts from her home at Sonning Common to London,[17] but none was to be published until the 1980s, when some of the watercolours were used in greetings cards, and, later, posters and, now, calendars. Others came into the hands of Church's successor at Oxford, Arthur Clapham (1904–1990), who reproduced an unpublished one with others from *Types of flo-*

22 Manna ash *Fraxinus ornus* L. (Oleaceae). Photograph by A.H. Church. "Graft scar of specimen in the Bot. Gard. Oxford, 1908"; "Grafted on the Common Ash it frequently develops more rapidly than the stock, and thus produces a huge graft scar: a good example is seen in the Oxford Botanic Garden: this specimen is over 100 years old" (Church MSS, *Types of floral mechanism*). See fig. 11.

ral mechanism in *The biology of flowers* (1935), which he wrote with William James. In their preface they wrote:

"Neither of the present authors has had more than the slightest personal contact with Dr. A.H. Church, lately of this department. It nevertheless remains true that his influence on the preparation of this little book has been very great, as any one who knows his work will realize. For various reasons Dr. Church's own writings and drawings are much less easily available than could be desired and one excuse for the present volume is that we hope it may help disseminate the methods he did so much to improve."

But no more of Church's text was ever published. Quotations from it are in the captions to many of the plates in this book, and more complete excerpts on waterlilies follow here with some of the appropriate illustrations from The Natural History Museum (see also plate 18) They give the reader a flavour of the intellectually challenging but in many ways delightful as well as informative style of Church's work.

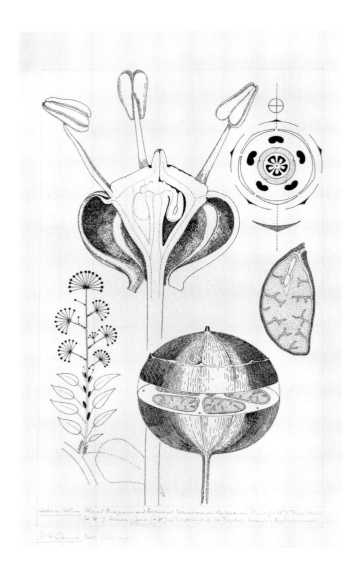

23 Ivy *Hedera helix* L. (Araliaceae). Unpublished figure for *Types of floral mechanism*, ink on Bristol board, 1911. Median section of flower, floral diagram, inflorescence-structure, fruit and seed in section in the plane of the raphe. Ivy, native in Europe and western Asia, flowers late and is pollinated by wasps and moths; the very nutritious fruits ripen over winter and are an important food-source for young birds in spring.* Long considered to counteract the effects of alcohol, ivy is drawn in the chaplet of Bacchus and was used as a sign for a tavern. *Hedera* is the Latin name for the plant; *helix* is Greek for spiral and was another name used by the Romans for the plant.

NOTES

1 Corner (1981), pp. 5–6
2 Church (1908), p. iii.
3 Corner (1981), p. 4.
4 Mabberley, *Bauer* (1999).
5 Mabberley (1981), p. vi.
6 Corner (1981), p. 5.
7 Church (1908), pp. iii–iv.
8 Mabberley (1981), pp. 250–52.
9 Some may be among those in the University of Sheffield (see Mabberley (1981), p. 252).
10 L.B. 2269, Archives, Oxford University Press. Sadly, this file was heavily 'weeded' in 1927.

11 L.B. 2269, Archives, Oxford University Press. The blocks were destroyed in 1962.
12 *Journal of Botany*, 46, 1908, pp. 237–38.
13 Church to J. Britten (?), 7 July 1908, Autograph Collection, Department of Botany, The Natural History Museum.
14 Corner (1981), p. 5.
15 L.B. 2269, Archives, Oxford University Press; from Church, 19 November 1925; to Church, 21 November 1925.
16 L.B. 2269, Archives, Oxford University Press.
17 Grace Grattan to J. Ramsbottom, 23 September 1937 (Keeper's Correspondence 1937, The Natural History Museum).

Unpublished extract on waterlilies from
Types of floral mechanism

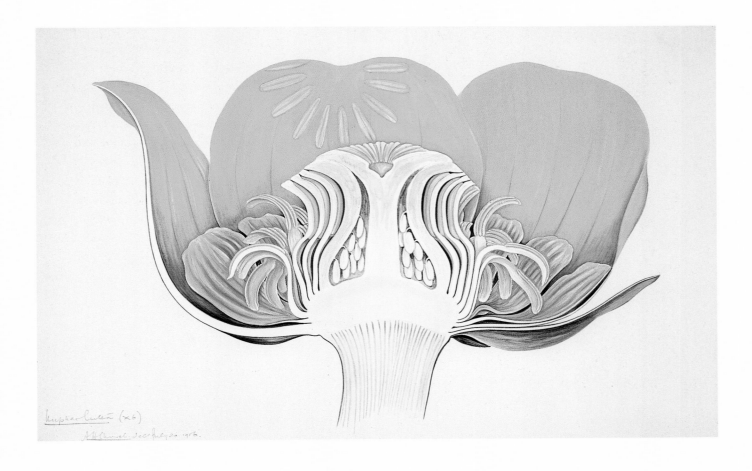

PLATE 22 Brandy-bottle *Nuphar luteum* (L.) Sm. (Nymphaeacae), 20 July 1906. Found throughout much of the northern hemisphere, brandy-bottle has flowers that emit an alcoholic smell (hence its common name), attractive to pollinating beetles.* Despite this, in the thirteenth century the flowers were carved as wooden roof-bosses in both Westminster Abbey and Bristol Cathedral.† Note the impression of the stigmatic surface on the unfolding central tepal. *Nuphar* is from the Persian *nufar; luteum* = yellow.

"*Nymphaea alba* ... Although there is no structural attempt to eliminate autogamy [selfing], special adaptations which will promote cross-pollination are observable in the following respects:- (1) The flowers are definitely protogynous, the stigmatic papillae being normally only receptive on the first day of expansion. These secrete a certain amount of fluid which accumulates in the groove around the axial peg-growth, and may fill the stigmatic cup. With this functional period is associated a slight fragrant odour; on succeeding days the stigmatic surface is dry, the hairs wither and become discoloured, and there is no scent. (2) The non-dehiscence of the anthers on the first day of exposure is probably due to the massive character of the succulent connective-regions with which the aqueous epidermal system is in communication. — The first-day flower is thus in the carpellary stage, and cross-pollination by insect agency becomes possible; and more probable in that only one blossom is normally functional on one rhizome at a time. ... Pollination may be effected by small flies and beetles which range over the surface of ponds. Small pollen-taking flies appear to be the most general visitors, as also very small bees and these may be found drowned in the stigmatic fluid. ... As the fruits approach maturity they turn yellow, and rise towards the surface owing to the excretion of gases in their spongy tissues. The method of dehiscence, and dispersal of the seeds, may be readily studied by picking almost mature fruits as they begin to change colour, and keeping them under observation in a glass of water. Dehiscence may be hastened by slightly warming the water. The fruits possess a succulent outer wall, and the loculi are completely filled with seeds, each invested by a membranous sack-like aril which springs from the funicle and forms a bell-shaped mantle twice as long as the seed itself ... dehiscence takes place along an irregular line which follows the weakest part of the fruit-wall, i.e., that along the line of attachment of the stamens, and is brought about by the enlargement of the soft tissues of the inner part of the wall. Simultaneously a considerable amount of gas is excreted by the membranous layers, and the membranous arils of the seeds; the internal part of the fruit thus expands, and tends to throw off the upper portion of the wall by an irregular split. The broken edges recurve as the tension of the outer wall is relieved, and the membrane-covered loculi are exposed. These membranous layers rapidly disintegrate in water, and the cells of the inner part of the fruit wall, having exhausted themselves in gas-excretion soon decompose; the whole mass of seeds is thus liberated, and rises to the surface of the water. Air-bubbles enclosed under the aril-membranes give the seeds a white glistening appearance, so that the mass of black seeds floating by means of loose air-containing arils presents a general resemblance to a mass of frog-spawn; so close in fact, that if it only took place at the proper time of the year, it might have been claimed as an example of 'mimicry'.

Nuphar lutea [*sic*]. ... The bulky rhizomes which may attain a diameter of 4–5 inches remain imbedded in the mud which they convert into a peculiar black slime, the upper surface being just sufficiently exposed to become green ... as in the case of *Nymphaea*, the plant presents similar adaptations to a habitat in ponds and moving streams. The globular flower-buds are borne on stout stalks containing a spongy network of air-lacunae; they arise at the end of the leaf-formation of the season's growth or somewhat irregularly. ... As the flowers are borne usually close together, and only few (2–3) are provided in the growth of the current year, the flowering period is often extremely restricted.

Theoretical Considerations

The Waterlilies constitute so clearly isolated a group of plants, their flowers are so large and beautiful, and their special features so striking, that like the Orchids they present a fascination of their own, and stand apart from the rest of the Vegetable Kingdom. ... the Waterlily-type combines extreme specialization for an

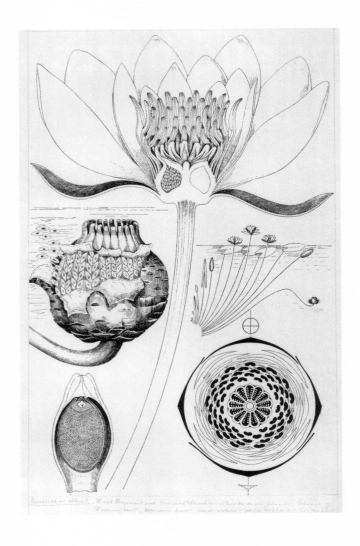

24 White waterlily *Nymphaea alba* L. (Nymphaeaceae). Unpublished figure (intended for Part II), ink on Bristol board, 1906. "Floral Diagram and Sectional Elevation in the median plane. Scheme of flowering shoot: Dehiscing fruit, and section of seed in the plane of the raphe" (Church MSS, *Types of floral mechanism*). Like many aquatic plants common around Oxford in Church's time, the white waterlily,* a species found throughout Eurasia, is now in decline there.

aquatic environment with a very generalised form of floral mechanism, and it is requisite to distinguish between factors of secondary specialization and conditions which may be regarded as really primitive, and pointing to an extremely archaic type of Angiosperm flower. Thus the close agreement of the plan of rhizome-construction with such a biological growth-form as that of the Common Fern [*Dryopteris*] has been already indicated; and it is clear that the ancestral form was an inhabitant of the shady undergrowth of forests, and the sides of streams and ponds, before it became relegated to the entirely aquatic mode of life. Forms of Nymphaea will still flower in marshy situations as the soil dries up. ... Nuphar flourishes in shallow water, with large erect aerial leaves, and Euryale, the most specialized type of

the alliance, is flowered most satisfactorily in a melon-frame.

Within the limits of the present genus *Nymphaea*, it appears clear that at an extremely early date, and probably before the plants left the land, the floral mechanism stood committed to the protogynous specialization of a fly-chamber type of flower. This being again the essential character of the mechanism of *Nuphar*, as also of *Euryale* & *Victoria*. The method is again then suggestive of the peculiarities noted in the spathe of many Aroid inflorescences; this being probably the result of a convergence of mechanism adapted to the conditions of insect-life in the undergrowth of ancient forests." (Church MSS, *Types of floral mechanism*).

PLATE 23 Pitcher plant, *Sarracenia purpurea* L. (Sarraceniaceae).* 7 May 1905. Native to eastern North America, and now naturalized in Ireland and Switzerland, the pitcher plant is named after Michel Sarrazin de l'Etang (1659–1734), physician at the court of Quebec, who sent a plant to the French botanist Tournefort. The major pollinators are newly emerged *Bombus* queen bees.† The pitchers are modified leaves, their lips with nectariferous veins, attractive to flying insects, inside; the inner surfaces have downward pointing hairs and smooth slip zones so that captured insects cannot retreat. By 1791 it was realized that the plant was carnivorous and in 1829 Burnett argued that it digested food in the same way as animals do: it is now known that a proteolytic enzyme, leucine aminopeptidase, is produced by glands in the pitchers. Certain midge larvae are resistant and feed on detritus inside; a maggot living at the surface of the water inside eats half of all captured prey.‡

'Thalassiophyta'

25 Professor Sir Frederick Keeble, FRS (1870–1952)

In 1910 Church was appointed university lecturer in the Department of Botany: the demonstratorship went to one of his pupils, Wilfred Hiley (1886–1961), later lecturer in forest economics. For Church's elementary course, taught at the University Museum, there were some thirty-two undergraduates but the advanced courses attracted only between eight and eleven students, though there were classes of thirty-three for his course for forestry students.[1] By 1912 Church was also giving classes on Indian botany.[2]

Despite the disappointment of *Types of floral mechanism*, Church continued his original research work, besides his crippling teaching load. Albert Seward, professor of botany at Cambridge, suggested to him that he investigate *Welwitschia mirabilis*, the extraordinary gymnosperm found in the deserts of south-western Africa, where it derives its moisture largely from seafogs. A turnip-like plant with just two leaves, it lives for up to 1500 years;[3] its relationship with angiosperms has long been debated.

Church set about studying its 'floral mechanism'. His paper was communicated by Seward to the Royal Society in December 1913 and was read on 5 February 1914. It was printed and made available as a separate reprint in June 1914.[4] A model of cautious investigation, which combined an assessment of previous work with original observations on development, the masterly paper is accompanied by Church's own drawings.[5] In conclusion, he wrote:

"These interesting Gymnospermous flowers present no indication whatever of any relation to the carpellary flowers of Angiosperms, in which, though even now a majority may have replaced the original megasporophylls by new ovary-formations not involving leaf-members, vestigial carpels usually remain to indicate the progression. The general resemblance is merely that of a parallel progression of physiological mechanism devoted to seed-production, on special non-assimilatory shoot-systems conventionally called 'flowers'."

Within a few weeks Britain was at war with Germany. The following term saw the end of Oxford as Church had known it and led to the greatest crisis in his life. In

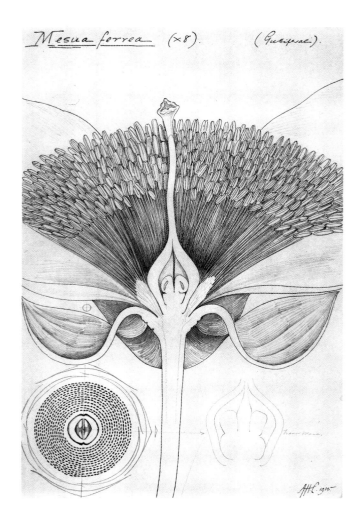

26 Ironwood *Mesua ferrea* L. (Guttiferae). Left: demonstration drawing for lectures on Indian botany: half flower and floral diagram, ink and wash on paper, 1915; right: original sketch, pencil on paper (Bodleian Library, University of Oxford, Church MSS II. 2(b) iv). "Evergreen forest-tree of E. Bengal and Assam, much planted; Flowers large white and *Cistus-like*, with golden-yellow tassel of anthers, but *tetramerous*; stamens to 1,000 on collar-growth ...."* *Mesua* commemorates John of Damascus (Johannes Mesue, 777–857), physician and botanist; *ferrea* means iron. The tree is sacred in India and its very hard timber has been much used for railway sleepers there.†

Michaelmas term 1914 most Oxford undergraduates enlisted in the armed forces: many college fellows and servants did the same, in a patriotic fervour difficult to understand today. By 1915 the undergraduate population was down by two-thirds and by 1918 only 12% remained.

The drop in tuition fees led to difficult times for the colleges: professors and readers agreed to a reduction in their emoluments to help university finances. In 1915 Hiley had enlisted[6] and by 1918 Church was sometimes 'lecturing' to classes of just one student.[7] Where five undergraduates had taken honours botany final examinations in 1914, there was only one in each of the examinations of 1915 and 1916 (when Church was examiner), both of them Indians: there were no more finalists in botany until 1921.[8]

The elegant new Examination Schools building in the High Street became a military hospital. Where Oxford had been a city of the high-spirited young and privileged in the Edwardian period, its streets were now full of the wounded, its lights dimmed against the raids of zeppelins, the 101 evening strikes of Christ Church's Great Tom silenced, and the spirit of those who had remained broken by news of the rising toll at the Front.[9]

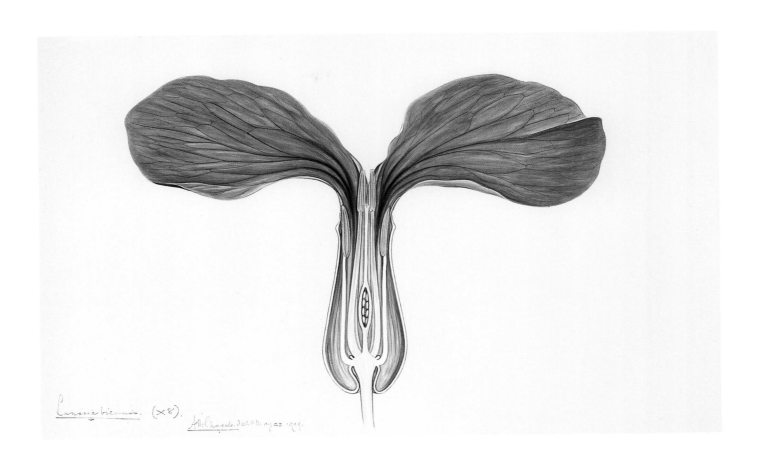

Lunaria biennis. (×8).

A.H. Church del. May 23 1909.

PLATE 24 Honesty *Lunaria annua* L. [L. biennis] (Cruciferae). 23 May 1909. Native to Mediterranean Europe, honesty has been long grown in gardens for its pretty flowers and the large fruits with satiny paper-white septa, whole branches being dried for winter decoration.* In Guernsey it is hung up in wardrobes for good luck. The flowers are visited for nectar by butterflies and long-tongued bees, and for pollen by smaller insects: if all fails, they self-pollinate.† Although the plant contains many alkaloids, the roots are said to be edible and the seeds are rich in monounsaturated fatty acids.‡ Honesty is naturalized in northern Europe, being recorded from Oxfordshire first in 1886,§ and North America. The common name is said to come from the transparent quality of the seed-pods. *Lunaria* is from the Latin *luna*, moon, also an allusion to the septum, another country name being moon pennies.

Spiraea opulifolia (×15)
A.H. Church del. June 16 1906

PLATE 25 Ninebark *Physocarpus opulifolius* (L.) Maxim. [Spiraea opulifolia] (Rosaceae). 16 June 1906. Native to central and eastern North America, this cultivated shrub gets its common name from the layers of flaking bark. The generic name comes from the Greek *physa*, a bladder, and *karpos*, fruit, an allusion to the inflated follicular fruit; *opulifolius* means with leaves like *Viburnum opulus* L. (Guelder rose).

PLATE 26 Peony *Paeonia officinalis* L. (Paeoniaceae). 27 May 1905. "The Paeony is indigenous in the mountains of Central and Southern Europe, extending from Spain to the Caucasus, growing wild in stony places at a considerable elevation" (Church MSS, *Types of floral mechanism*); it was introduced to Britain before 1548. It figures in Albrecht Dürer's *Maria mit vielen Tieren* (Virgin and Child with a Multitude of Animals), painted *c.* 1503 and now hanging in the Albertina in Vienna.* "The flowers are laid down in the previous summer, and perennate practically fully formed, the mass being 6–7 mm in diameter in the winter months. ... A large central tassel of slender-stalked orange anthers being grouped around a purple-crested stigma which acts as a rigid landing-stage, while the petal-laminae constitute a protective chamber of a firm bowl-like character. The stigmatic surface is at an elevation only very slightly higher than the anthers, and any large insect alighting on the central mass of members must convey pollen to the receptive papillae. The flowers are thus accessible to a wide range of insects who visit the blossoms for the sake of pollen, or for the prospect of shelter or honey [*i.e.* nectar] -supply. The petals increase in size very considerably during the first few days of expansion, and then a rapid growth-extension presents a daily periodicity for a short time; the flowers then close towards night and open again next morning." *Paeonia* is a modified form of the Greek name Paion, a pupil of the mythical Aesculapius, and whom Pluto changed into a plant because of his cures; *officinalis* refers to its being sold in shops, *i.e.* by apothecaries.

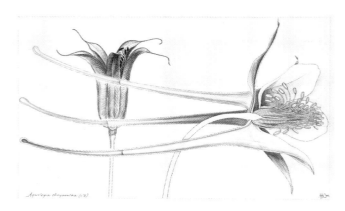

27 *Aquilegia chrysantha* A. Gray (Ranunculaceae). Unpublished figure, ink and wash on Bristol board (Church MSS, *Types of floral mechanism*, Part 2), 1906. Native to the southern United States, *A. chrysantha* (from the Greek for golden-flowered) is one of the garden columbines with long straight spurs. "General consideration of such a floral structure shows at once that the great length of spur (40–60 mm) places the honey [*i.e.* nectar] far beyond the reach of any bee, even when the tubes are half-filled, and that the flower must be pollinated by long-tongued moths. In this connection it is interesting to note that the horizontal projection of the blossom, the loose dusty tassel of stamens, as also the tendency to zygomorphy … may be correlated with such insect-visitation, while the fragrance of the bloom and its clear pale colour, which renders it increasingly conspicuous as a white star-like blossom at dusk, when anthocyanin pigments soon lose their effectiveness, are minor features which may become beneficial from the stand-point of moth-pollination."

The city became a military camp, with soldiers billeted in the rooms previously the preserve of the élite. As the War wore on, the columns of the *Oxford University Gazette* became crammed with black-edged announcements of the 'casualties'.

In the winter of 1915–16, Church's daughter Rosemary contracted tuberculosis. Then came a second tragedy, in that his wife, Emma, who, according to family tradition, had taken to furtive concealing of fragments of food between the cushions of furniture, fell ill with botulism. In Church's presence at 246 Iffley Road, she died of "gastroenteritis excited by ptomaine poisoning" on 25 January 1916.[10] Exactly two months later, after three months' suffering, Rosemary too died, at the Radcliffe Infirmary, Oxford, with Church again at the bedside. Emma and Rosemary were buried in the same grave at Rose Hill Cemetery, Oxford.[11] In January 1917 Church wrote a simple will, with his sister-in-law Elizabeth Coverdale as executrix, leaving everything to his only surviving close relative, his third daughter, Grace:[12] he never changed it.

The War brought on depression in Church and he began to believe that concentrating on botany had led to the neglect of his family: he teetered on insanity.[13] His misery was compounded by the deaths of so many of his friends and pupils in the battlefields of France. By the end of hostilities, roughly one in five of the Oxford men who had enlisted had been killed. This was a higher proportion than in the country as a whole because so many of them were officers, a group with a relatively high fatality rate. Poulton's son was killed[14] and Jesus College lost 14% of its old members and undergraduates, while those colleges with higher proportions of officers lost even more; Corpus Christi, for example, lost 25%.[15]

But with the end of the War came a huge outpouring of Church's work in published form. He decided to put into print his ideas on plant evolution, ideas delivered and refined in lectures. In July 1919 he could write

PLATE 27 *Aquilegia canadensis* L. (Ranunculaceae). 21 June 1908. Native to eastern North America, it was being grown in England by John Tradescant the Elder before 1640. The long spurs secrete nectar; "Observations in America (Iowa, Illinois) show that the flowers are visited by 'Tobacco Sphinx Moths', which do not work the flowers of *A. vulgaris* with curved spurs, but also by the 'Rubythroated Hummingbird'. These birds, poised in air under the inverted blossoms, scatter the pollen widely as they probe the vertical nectary-tubes" (Church MSS, *Types of floral mechanism*, Part II). The generic name, originally 'Aquilina', comes from the Latin *aquila*, eagle, a reference to flower supposedly resembling eagle's claws; the common name for species of *Aquilegia* is columbine, a reference to the petals and sepals resembling doves' heads and wings (*columba* is dove in Latin).

to Antony Gepp (1862–1955), algologist at The Natural History Museum,[16] about what had become *Oxford Botanical Memoirs 1: The building of the autotrophic flagellate* (1919, 2s.).[17] Gepp was to become a sounding board for Church's ideas; Church wrote to him every few days, and his letters of their correspondence, surviving at The Natural History Museum, comprise the most complete series known. They provide a valuable insight into British botany and botanists of the period. Of the *Memoir*, Church wrote that it had been rejected by *Science Progress* and that he had considered it too long for the museum's *Journal of Botany*, "so I have run it out myself at Oxford (I hope to do some more like it)". In concluding it, he wrote:

"The story of the origin of a simple autotrophic plant-cell, briefly indicated in twenty pages or so, each involving a special volume of data and further elaboration, may suffice to express in a condensed form a picture of the early struggles of elementary organism in the plankton-phase, in which all the more fundamental features of organism have been evolved, as leading to the benthic condition of Marine algae; and in all essentials surviving in the cell-organization of higher land-flora, as wall-mechanism, nuclear organization, phenomena of sexual fertilization, the development of the idea of the individual, and the isolation of races, living under new conditions of intense wastage, though retaining much of the older equipment otherwise wholly unintelligible."[18]

Gepp reviewed it in the *Journal of Botany*, writing: "Dr Church's pamphlet is written in a condensed style not

PLATE 28 Lupin *Lupinus polyphyllus* Lindl. (Leguminosae). 23 June 1908. "Indigenous to north West America, from Washington Territory to San Francisco, and discovered by [David] Douglas [1798–1834] who introduced seeds into this country. Plants were first raised in the Garden of the Horticultural Society (1827)" (Church MSS, *Types of floral mechanism*). With *L. arboreus* Sims, the tree-lupin of California, and perhaps other species, it is one of the parents of the modern Russell lupins, *L. x regalis* Bergmans, raised by George Russell, who began breeding them in 1911 when he was 60 years old: they were released to the trade in 1937.* "The keel-petals ... constitute the claw-like chamber enclosing the essential organs. ... The upper edges of the keel-petals are also folded and lightly fused ... the close adhesion is produced by the interlocking of minute cuticular ridges. ... The anthers dehisce in the bud before the standard petal commences to expand. ... The filaments now elongate ... pushing the pollen-mass more and more, in the course of the final adjustments, into the extreme apex of the claw, where finally the orange pollen-mass is just covered by the intensely pigmented tips of the keel-petals. The filaments employed in this ramming function acquire a special stout structure & the median posterior stamen which is not so employed remains short. ... The conical stigmatic apex is surrounded by a brush of long hairs and the whole structure is imbedded in the centre of the rammed mass of pollen. These stiff hairs are possibly fairly efficient in preventing the deposit of pollen on the stigmatic papillae, so long as no external agency affects the mechanism, and so long as the pollen mass is merely rammed forwards ... a very highly organized piston-type of mechanism. Thus on depressing the wing petals very gently, a worm-like thread of orange pollen appears pressed out of the keel tip. The hinge does not dislocate, but recovers owing to the strength of the keel-members; while the slight adhesion of the wings prevents lateral displacement. With care it may be observed that the mechanism may be worked, and a small supply of pollen extruded, as many as 40–50 times before the pollen-supply is all used up, and the style projects in a naked condition." The generic name is a classical one, perhaps derived from the Greek *lupe*, grief, and perhaps then referring to the bitter seeds of certain lupin species, or from the Latin *lupus*, a wolf, from the superstition that they reduced the fertility of the soil, though, like most legumes, they actually improve it as they have nitrogen-fixing bacteria in root nodules; *polyphyllus* means many-leaved, referring to the many leaflets.

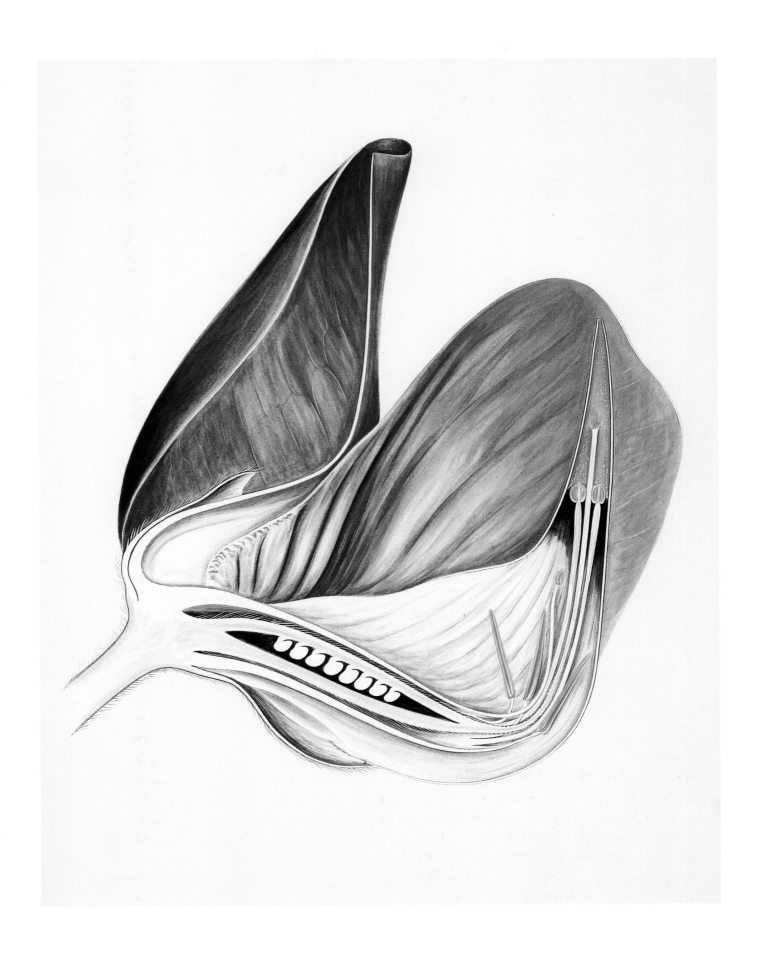

easy to digest at the first reading, but it is logical and presents a fascinating study of the origin and progression of plant life and all that it involves, which will be welcomed and enjoyed by all students of biology".[19] Such prose is indeed difficult to follow (an anonymous reviewer in *Nature* referred to it as "repellent language"),[20] and even Church admitted to Gepp, "it is calculated to give one a headache if taken all at once". This gentle self-mockery permeates his gossipy yet authoritative letters.

John Ramsbottom, then mycologist at the museum, wrote of Church, "One of the outstanding features of recent botanical literature is the sudden outburst of publication on the part of the author".[21] Indeed, Church was publishing book reviews and a whole torrent of papers in almost every issue of the *Journal of Botany*.[22] The most important were phycological papers and Gepp helped him with them: five appeared in 1919 alone. Two of these were historical reviews of the study of different groups. He also produced bibliographical and biographical papers based on historical materials in the department library: on Baxter's *British phaenogamous botany* and on Brunfels and Fuchs (see plate 47). However, Church was not entirely pleased with Ramsbottom's words: "I was much amused by Ramsbottom's patronizing remarks ... & to think I had never even heard of Ramsbottom before! I have one or two gibes for him in the next memoir. I always drop in any jokes at any odd corner."[23]

Church was also preparing for print 'schedules' for lectures, particularly the forestry classes, but also advanced ones "including all Mendelism on one page", "purely of local interest and adapted to what can be done at the Oxford Dept. where things are in rather a bad way".[24] Indeed, Church was very critical of Vines, who was about

to retire. Church wrote to James Britten (1846–1924), editor of the *Journal of Botany* issued by The Natural History Museum:

"[Frederick] *Keeble* [(1870–1952), Director of the Royal Horticultural Society's garden at Wisley] is the new Professor, quite the best choice of a poor lot. No 'Professor' was in for the job — only second raters, some kind but misguided friends wanted me to have it, but I am the last person for such a job. I have only realized lately what a dog's life a Professor can have. ... Keeble is no great scientist with a message, but he is a very smart 'official' & clearheaded, knowing how to set about things in a professional style. ... He has interviewed the great [George Claridge] Druce [1850–1932, curator of the Fielding Herbarium in the department since 1895] & told him he will be expected to teach what he knows (if he knows anything worth teaching, poor Druce is in danger of being found out)."[25]

Seward had favoured one of the other candidates, Arthur Tansley,[26] ecology lecturer in his own department, who eventually got the post on Keeble's resignation in 1927. On his own career, Church wrote of how he had begun "on a poorer plane, & once on a time I had hoped to have risen to the Nat. Hist. Museum staff, & now end at Oxford. After all Oxford is better I think than Govt. service for a happy irresponsible person."[27]

But soon Keeble, like Vines before him, was to become the butt of many of Church's jokes and complaints, even though he sympathized with him as another widower with a teenaged daughter. He confided to Britten:

PLATE 29 *Cypripedium reginae* Walter [*C. spectabile*] (Orchidaceae). 23 June 1906. Native to northeastern North America, this orchid was introduced to cultivation in Britain in 1731. Nectar secreted in the pouch-like lip attracts small bees, which enter it but cannot escape that way because of the slippery sides of the lip and its inrolled edges; they make their way towards the back of the flower, where they can grip on hairs at the base of the lip and then pass by the stigma where pollen brought from other flowers is deposited, before brushing against the anthers and collecting new pollen to take to other flowers.* The generic name is from *Kypris* and refers to the Cyprian goddess, *i.e.* Venus (associated with Aphrodite); *pedilon* is slipper, hence the common name lady's slipper orchids used for orchids in this and allied genera; *reginae* means "of the queen".

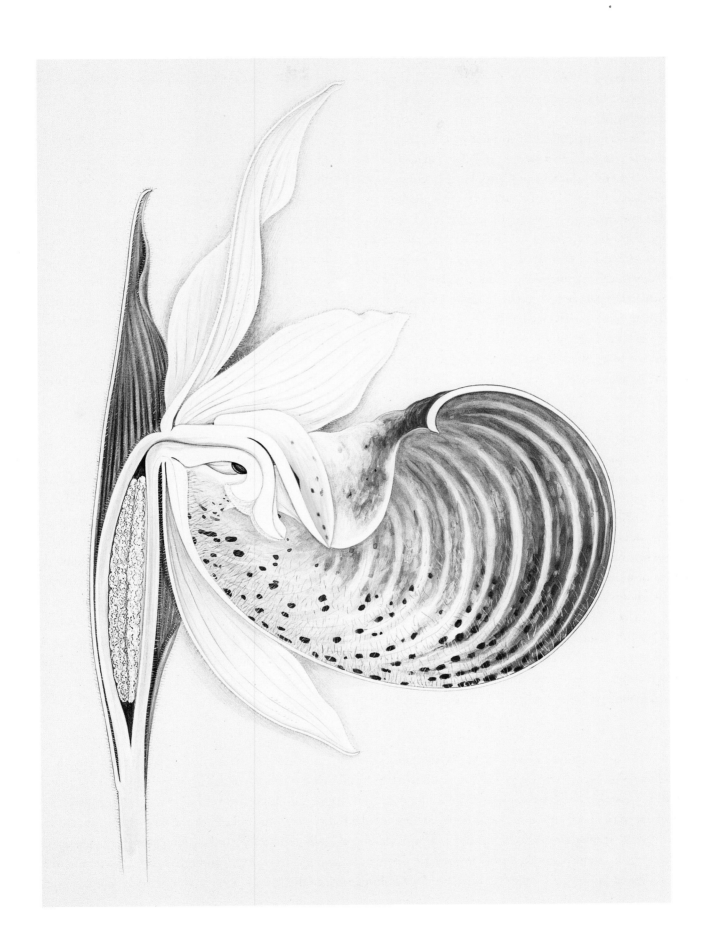

"The Professor is away as long as possible, but he will have to settle down if he intends to do anything. Between you & me, I think that if he doesn't get on he will clear out with a Govt. job … he has begun rather awkwardly by making friends with Vines whom all progressives detest, & I see he is going to have a house *outside* Oxford (Boar's Hill) this is also fatal. It was Vines's mistake. If you are at Oxford, you *must be* in the centre, or you lose touch of people, who won't take the trouble to see you … the last joke about Vines is that he is taking his *chair* with him, into retirement. The old chap never had a decent private room, nor even a work room, let alone a 'reception room' like any decent professor – only a bare room he called 'an office' with a study chair, a hearth rug, & an old bureau to keep his cheque-book in … these things he brought with him 30 years ago. … Poor Keeble will have to buy a new chair."[28]

Church had come to detest the philosophy that Vines had stood for, and wrote to Gepp of the scientific outlook of a correspondent, "anti-German as I am, also anti-Vines, who brought in the German domination [of botany] and all its stupidity & *failure to understand* what the evolution of Darwin *really meant*".[29]

Oxford Botanical Memoir 2, by H.J. Denham, on cotton in pre-Linnaean literature, had appeared in July 1919: it is the only one of the fifteen *Memoirs* not by Church, who called it "very dry".[30] The later schedules were to appear as *Memoir 4, Elementary notes on structural botany* (1919), at 2s., with Church later noting to Gepp, "I think it might sell & help pay for the others."[31] But in writing about the autotrophic flagellate (he wittily called it "auto flag"),[32] he had already sent to Gepp drafts of what was to be *Memoir 3* and to make his name, "enclosing another stunt of the same type, only worse".[33] He added in August:

"It takes *me* 3 days to read over so I hope it will last you to Xmas! As I always run in 2 or 3 more pages every time I look at it, it is very uneconomical, seeing it has to be paid for. But the wonder of the story only grows more and more … one can only sit and gasp or gape. I stick over it myself until I get a new point. Only yesterday I ran in a page because for the first time I tumbled to what a *cambium* really meant."[34]

He wrote:

"One only gets 1 or 2 ideas a day & it is slow work collecting them. Yet I have found out that is the only way of getting them. … I had not read Darwin's *autobiography* before last week. It is very illuminating after the sort of rubbish biographers compile. I was pleased to find he had the idea of scribbling down

PLATE 30 Carolina allspice *Calycanthus floridus* L. (Calycanthaceae). 25 June 1905. "Indigenous to North America (N. Carolina to Georgia, Alabama to Mississippi) … Introduced into this country by Catesby in 1726, and still cultivated somewhat sparingly for the sake of its peculiar fragrant brown-purple flowers … [an] odour which has been compared with that of crushed stawberries. … The shape of the receptacle-crater is seen on cutting the flower longitudinally, and presents a remarkably beautiful example [but] has no necessary connection with the pollination mechanism, but is correlated with the necessity for the protection of the ovules, and the subsequent development of a 'fruit' structure around the developing seeds. … The flowers are remarkable for their extremely early development, the young blossoms of the succeeding season being laid down before those of the current season are fully functional. The flowers possess no honey [*i.e.* nectar] but offer copious pollen supplies inside a fairly protected chamber type of blossom … the floral structure clearly suggests that small insects, such as flies, beetles &c. may be attracted to this chamber by the peculiar scent and purple colouration of the perianth members; and that these remain inside the flower until the pollen is shed" (Church MSS, *Types of floral mechanism*). The bark was formerly used medicinally and as a substitute for cinnamon.* The generic name is from the Greek *kalyx*, calyx, and *anthos*, flower, as perianth segments are all dull like sepals; *floridus* means profusely flowering.

28 *Dactylorhiza fuchsii* with pollinating bee, the pollinia in the initial (dotted lines) and final position: their stalks are attached to the insect's head and bend so that the pollen bags are in a position to contact the stigma of the next flower. Unpublished figure, ink and wash on Bristol board, 10 July 1900, for *Types of floral mechanism*.*

29 '*Apis*'. Working pencil drawing of bee with pollinia in final position (Church MSS V (iv) f. 128, Bodleian Library, University of Oxford).

ideas as they came, in illegible writing, & then sorting them out later. Doing this sets the subconscious mind at work & the result turns up often in a few days."[35]

He was weaving together a history of all land flora from its marine origins. Clearly seeing that land-plants are just rather specialized forms of marine life, he effectively anticipated the cladistic view of modern botanists, writing, "The next generation of botanists may be *all* algologists."[36]

This was *Thalassiophyta and the subaerial transmigration*,[37] 'thalassiophyta' being Church's Latinization of the French *thalassiophytes*, a term used early in the nineteenth century for sea-plants. It seems that he had at first intended that it be published serially in the *Journal of Botany*; Church noted to Gepp:

"I am glad Mr Britten sent back the 'Transmigration'. It was designed for *12* monthly parts & in the J. of B. would have taken *18* months to come out in 'supplements' & now I can get it done in 8 from the time I sent it. [Arthur] Tansley [editor of the *New Phytologist*] also refused Chap. I. I am glad it is not in the beastly print of the *New Phyt*. & worse paper."[38]

PLATE 31 Spotted orchid *Dactylorhiza fuchsii* (Druce) Soó [Orchis maculata] (Orchidaceae). 28 June 1906. Perhaps England's most common orchid, it is a rapid colonizer and is still common in Oxfordshire in damp permanent grassland, open woodland and scrub, including railway banks.* Exudates from the stigma are attractive to pollinating bees. The generic name comes from the Greek *daktylos* – finger – and *rhiza* – root, referring to the finger-like tubers compared with the rounded ones in *Orchis*. Druce, who distinguished the common spotted orchid from *D. maculata* (L.) Soó, which is rare in Oxfordshire, named it after Leonhard Fuchs (1501–1566), professor of medicine at Tübingen, Germany; see plate 47. Fuchs figured the orchid in his *De historia stirpium* (1542, p. 703) as 'Satyrium Royale femelle'.

Dictamnus Fraxinella (×4)
Arthur H. Church. July 1 1904.

PLATE 32 Dittany, *Dictamnus albus* L. (D. fraxinella). 1 July 1904. An Elizabethan introduction from Europe, dittany is wild from central and southern Europe eastwards to China. Both the Latin and common names come from the Greek name for a Cretan species of *Origanum*, possibly linked to Mount Dhikte there; *alba* = white, referring to the flower-colour of some forms. By 1756 it was known that the oils produced by the glands over much of the plant are inflammable and that when lit the oil burns off leaving the plant unharmed, hence the common name 'burning bush'; some people are allergic to it.

PLATE 33 Snapdragon *Antirrhinum majus* L. (Scrophulariaceae). 4 July 1903. Native to southwest Europe, where it is very variable, including some semi-scandent forms with grapple-like leaves,* it is naturalized in Britain. Such a plant growing on a wall in Oxford was the subject of some moral reflections by Cardinal Newman.† Only large insects such as bees can force open the flower to get to the nectar and pollen. The generic name comes from the Greek, roughly meaning counterfeiting a snout, an allusion to the flower-shape; *major, majus* is bigger, by comparison with Linnaeus's *Antirrhinum minus*, *i.e. Chaenorhinum minus* (L.) Lange, the small toadflax.

30 George Claridge Druce (1850–1932). "A confirmed bachelor and looked the part", whose "failings arose from his pronounced individuality".* His handwriting 's "main characteristic was that it was always open to several interpretations".† Druce ran a retail chemist's shop in the High Street in Oxford, a resort for many desperate undergraduates, and was mayor in 1900. He bequeathed his herbarium of 250,000 specimens, now part of the Fielding–Druce Herbarium in the Department of Plant Sciences, to the university and left funds for taxonomic research, though these were misused for many years; the first Druce fellow in plant taxonomy (David J. Mabberley [born 1948]) was not elected until 1973.

He sent Gepp proof sheets for comment: "It gets dry later on but brightens up at the end. ... I am limiting it to *100* pages".[39] It starts with:

"*The beginnings of Botany are in the sea*; and as it becomes more obvious that the vegetation of the land has at some time originated from transmigrant phyto-benthon, and that the somatic organization of branched cellular axes, stem and root, with apical growth and mechanism of leaf-arrangement, as also the entire phenomena of space-form, are the *inherited equipment* of a preceding phase of existence in the wholly submerged environment of the sea; — while the cell-equipment of chloroplasts, starch-metabolism, flagellate gametes, nuclear phenomena, chromosomes, sexual reproduction and meiosis, are equally inherited mechanism of a still older phase of pelagic phyto-plankton, persisting practically unchanged throughout the benthic period, — it becomes necessary to present some mental picture, however sketchy and crude, of the means whereby such a transition may have become possible, at some early period of the world's history."

Church wrote to Gepp of it:

"But the opening page is a great joy. That big sentence is designed purposely ... I wrote out the first chapter *3* times before I tumbled to it. The word 'beginning' of course comes from Genesis I.1! & the alliteration of the *b* and the *s* is very fine. If you keep on repeating that line, you will see it is immortal!

The first chapter is a bit of a parody of [Frederick O.] Bower [*Origin of land flora*, 1908] ... Bower [(1855–1948), professor of botany at Glasgow] introduced using grandiloquent language, which is *a good thing*, it increases the dignity of botany among the sciences. So I go equally grandiloquent & invent a lot of *catch phrases*

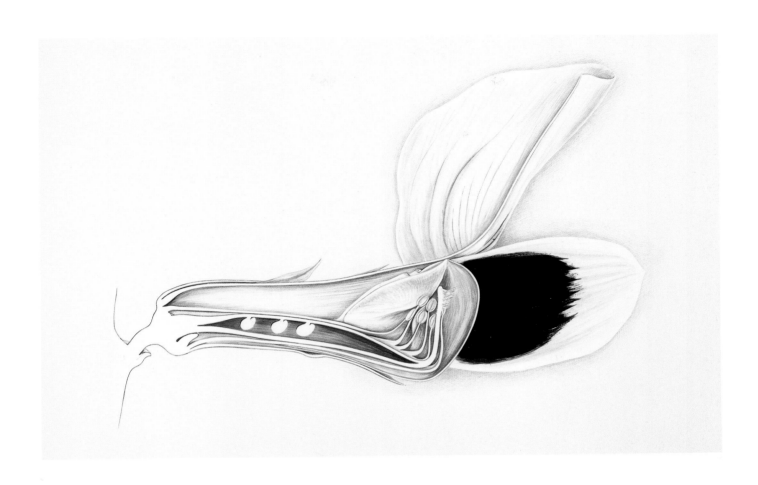

PLATE 34 Broad bean *Vicia faba* L. (Leguminosae). 6 July 1904. The flowers are pollinated by bees and for bumble bees are an important food-source before the clover season. Known only in cultivation, the broad bean is closely allied to *Vicia narbonensis* L., a bean from the Mediterranean through to Central Asia; primitive forms have black seeds. It was the bean of antiquity and a staple legume in medieval Europe, to be surpassed only with the introduction of the tropical *Phaseolus* beans of the New World civilizations. When eaten uncooked, broad beans can cause a form of hepatitis in many Italian and some Jewish people, due to a biochemical deficiency in red blood cells.* *Vicia* is Latin for vetch, a cognate word; *faba*, apparently cognate with the Faliscan (a kind of Etruscan) *haba*, was the Romans' name for the broad bean.†

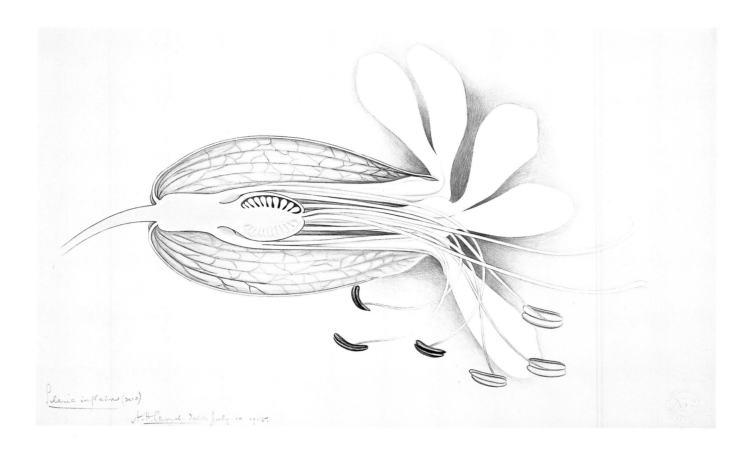

Silene inflata (x10)

H.H. Church. del. July 10 1905.

PLATE 35 Bladder campion *Silene vulgaris* (Moench) Garcke [S. inflata] (Caryophyllaceae). 10 July 1905. First recorded in Oxfordshire in 1666, bladder campion is native throughout Europe and western Asia to the Mediterranean. The night-scented flowers are pollinated by moths, notably the silver-Y, *Plusia gamma*, which turns to this and white campion, *S. latifolia* Poiret, when it is almost dark.* Though the moth's wings continue flapping during feeding, the flowers are gripped with the legs, so that a moth without forelegs has difficulty in feeding. The generic name *Silene* may be associated with the Sileni, the drunken slobbering companions of Bacchus,† though why is unclear.

PLATE 36 Sage *Salvia officinalis* L. (Labiatae). 12 July 1903. Native to the Mediterranean, sage is one of the most widely planted of culinary herbs, though in USA dried sage is often adulterated with leaves of *S. fruticosa*; the favour is due to terpineol and thujone.* The flowers are visited by many insects, especially bees by day but also, in the evening, by hawk-moths, which continue to feed on it until it is very dark indeed.† *Salvia* is the Romans' name for the plant and means safe, well or sound; *officinalis* indicates it was available from apothecaries and had medicinal qualities.

of my own (as the title & the chapter headings): e.g. Plankton, Benthon and Xerophyton is *deliberately designed*, on the analogy of Shadrach, Meschach & Abednego [Daniel 5:5]! Or to take a modern example, equally immortal, Athos, Porthos & Aramis [Dumas's *Three musketeers*]. The trick you see, is to have the first two words of the same class, the third a contrast with more syllables, You see I am a poet & have to attend to these little details. ... Literary people are often asses. I was dropped on once by the editor of 'Nature' for using *become* with a participle, when you can use it with an adjective, e.g. *become swollen* is all right, but *become inflated* is wrong: this is asinine! The important chapters of 'Transmigration' are *VIII* [Plankton, benthon] and *XII* [The algae of the transmigration] – they were written before any of the work you may have seen. In fact they made the others possible: it is difficult to follow them without the clue."[40]

Church wanted to make a splash and he asked Gepp to prepare a review from the proofs to appear in the *Journal of Botany* by the end of 1919: "I hope you will recommend your readers of the J. of Bot. to all *buy* the thing – it is quite cheap at 3/6 & will not pay costs. There is more stuff in it than 2 or 3 J. B.'s but as you say, it is *more worrying*."[41] Gepp sent him a review a few days later but Church feared Britten would not print it;[42] but he did, however, and Gepp came up trumps: "No such clear-sighted and thoughtful contribution to the study of plant-evolution has ever before been achieved. ... Dr Church's writings constitute a new era in the study of

botany ... and it is with the greatest interest that we look forward to further publications by so inspiring and suggestive a writer".[43] Tansley wrote a generally laudatory article based on *Thalassiophyta*, in his *New Phytologist*[44] while Church was proselytizing: "[Dunkinfield] Scott [the palaeobotanist] is much interested in it & we have talked it over, i.e. I do all the talking & he mostly agrees." He also gave a copy to Vines, "but he only grunted & won't be able to understand it for want of sheer knowledge of the facts!"[45] A few days later, he could write:

"Mr Scott likes 'Thalassiophyta' 'immensely' & Bower is critical & doesn't see it, but we are quite friends. He mentioned by 'disdainful criticism' of the Land Flora but I replied that I had been intentionally imitating his own style! & he agrees. Tansley told me that he also took the book to bed with him: it is so hard to go through 100 pages of somebody else's stuff in a hurry. I have found the Greek motto I meant to have put at the end: [Revelation 7:14 – 'These are they who have come out of the great tribulation'] Sorry now I didn't, although it isn't Homer."[46]

In sending a copy to Benjamin Daydon Jackson (1846–1927) at the Linnean Society, Church wrote, "I am sending another little joke, which I hope you will place before the Linn. Soc. ... Everybody should have a copy. It is quite up to the level of the 'Flagellate', & is really my bid for posthumous fame. If you gave Bower a gold medal for the Land Flora, this is quite up to a silver one, even in these days of high value!"[47] In explaining to

PLATE 37 Sweet william *Dianthus barbatus* L. (Caryophyllaceae). 15 July 1905. Native to southern Europe and now naturalized in China and North America,* sweet williams have been cultivated under that name since 1573, so, despite several later kings, and other, Williams, including saints, allegedly commemorated, it is much more likely that the name is a corruption of the French word *oeillet* to 'Willy' and hence William; 'wildewilliams' was the name for the native *Silene flos-cuculi* (L.) Clairv. (ragged robin).† The French word was formerly applied to wallflowers (*Erysimum cheiri* (L.) Crantz, Cruciferae), which are scented like pinks and their allies, to which the name is now applied, but also to species of *Silene*; it is derived from the Latin *ocellus*, a little eye, referring to the flower centre. Nonetheless, in the Orange lodges of Ulster, the sweet william has been transferred to William of Orange.‡ The generic name comes from the Greek *di-*, of Zeus or Jove, and *anthos*, flower; *barbatus* = bearded, referring to the bristly bracts and calyces.

Dianthus (×8)
"Sweet William"

Papaver somniferum (×2) ser.)
A.H. Church del. July 4 1904

PLATE 38 Opium poppy, *Papaver somniferum* L. (Papaveraceae). 17 July 1904. Perhaps derived from a wild species in south-west Asia, *P. somniferum* is not known outside cultivation. It was first grown in the western Mediterranean, but most is now in the region from Iran eastwards to China, and it is the most important drug plant in the world. Opium is the dried latex obtained by lancing immature capsules; it contains about twenty-five different alkaloids, especially morphine (9–17%).* The seeds contain no opium and are used on bread and in cakes. The plate may well represent ssp. *hortensis* (Hussenot) Corb., whose seeds are the source of poppy oil used in artists' paints and salad oils. The name *Papaver* comes from the Sumerian *pa pa* (see plate 5); *somniferum* = sleep-inducing.

PLATE 39 Rosebay willowherb *Epilobium angustifolium* L. (Onagraceae). 20 July 1904. Pollinated by bees which visit the lowermost flowers of the spike first, depositing pollen in those which have shed theirs and are now in the female phase (protandry), with a great deal of nectar. The bees cling to the projecting and somewhat drooping stamens and style, which bend under the weight, bringing the insects to an almost upright position, suggesting 'the way forward' for them;* they then move up the spike collecting pollen from younger flowers, before flying to another plant. First recorded in Oxfordshire in 1765,† *Epilobium angustifolium* is now found throughout the county: throughout England it has also greatly increased, in part due to the opening up of habitats, though there remains the possibility that new, more aggressive, genotypes have been introduced from elsewhere. Honey produced from the nectar is excellent. The young shoots have been eaten like asparagus, and an ale derived from the dried pith, while the leaves have been used in Russian tea.‡ The generic name comes from the Greek *epi*, upon, and *lobos*, pod, referring to the petals being inserted on the top of an inferior ovary; *angustifolium* = narrow-leaved. Rosebay was the old name for oleander (*Nerium oleander* L., Apocynaceae), later transferred to this plant because of its conspicuous flowers.

Britten at the museum why he had not put himself forward for Keeble's chair, he wrote, "No English Professor would have written *Thalassiophyta* for example, nor shd. I if I had been Professor! – just as in larger matters Darwin wd. not have done the *Origin* [*of Species*] if he had been a hack professor."[48]

The book, difficult to read as it was, even then, was a sensation, but Bower, who reviewed it in *Nature*, though generally enthusiastic, noted that it was "full of … interesting though bluff criticisms".[49] Church had heavily criticized Bower's works in reviews before and Bower did not forget the slights: in his *Sixty years of botany in Britain*, published in Church's lifetime (1930), Church is not even mentioned. Nonetheless, in January 1920 Church could write to Britten, "That immortal stunt is going very well. Scott is much struck by it, & Seward after reading it put my name down for F.R.S. – though it will not materialize, it was kind."[50] But he self-deprecatingly told Gepp, "Seward says No III 'fascinates' him so some people are easily pleased".[51]

He also told Gepp, "The *Bot. Memoirs* have simply gone on in a wholly irresponsible manner! I haven't the slightest idea whether they will go on beyond the year. It all depends on finding the money. It is easy enough to write them!"[52] He wrote to Britten early in 1920:

"I told you I wd. review my journalistic stunts at the end of the year. I find I am let in for about £200 so far, though it is only partly paid out as yet. But the results have been quite remarkable e.g. I have done about 15 papers including 2 or 3 of first class importance, & with very few 'homeless'. I have also gained many friends, whom I have not seen, & shd. not otherwise have known; also I have had some training in writing, which as you know I badly wanted.[53] Also I have bluffed £50 out of Vines & £100 out of the University! (as increases in salaries!). The papers are in many people's hands, & there is a great

stock of 'Schedules' i.e. on sale (I have printed 1000 copies of Bot. Mem. IV & V [*Elementary notes on the reproduction of angiosperms*; 2s.], & 500 of No. III, which may sell in course of time) & I expect to get more from Keeble, as the Dept. is a bit dependent on the *Schedules*. … So the expt. has been much more a success than one cd. have expected, even from a cash standpoint." [54]

He explained to Gepp:

"I did the first for sheer amusement in designing what I thought such a paper should be! in every detail – the Press will do exactly what one wants so long as one pays cash down! & they do their work very well and on the nail. No 3 was in the press exactly 2 months. It was all set up in a fortnight & all the rest in corrections. … the idea behind the Memoirs is that they may become *the* best English Botanical way of doing things. It makes one independent of both the *Annals* [*of Botany*] and the *Phil. Trans.* [*of the Royal Society*] i.e. the style is better than either: [Frederick] Hall [Printer to the University] at the Press, who prints the 'Annals' agrees that nobody with any taste or discrimination has ever had charge of it: & it merely follows the old grooves (and very expensive they are too). Mine is on *cheap* paper and the cheapest available print & cheapest cover: it only wants taste to choose the 'presentable'." [55]

Church had drawn up plans for remodelling the department's buildings and wrote, "I think my publication stunts really are advertising the place a bit (also A.H.C.) & it is up to Keeble to go ahead if he can get his domestic problems straightened out. Both he & Mrs K [Keeble had just married the actress Lillah Macarthy (1875–1960)], I should say, are too much Londoners to settle down at Oxford."[56] At the same time Church was

PLATE 40 Silk vine *Periploca graeca* L. (Asclepiadaceae/Apocynaceae). 23 July 1907. Native to southeast Europe and western Asia, the silk vine is a deciduous climber grown in gardens. The generic name comes from the Greek *periploke*, which means twisted or woven around, referring to the twining habit of the plant; *graeca* means Greek.

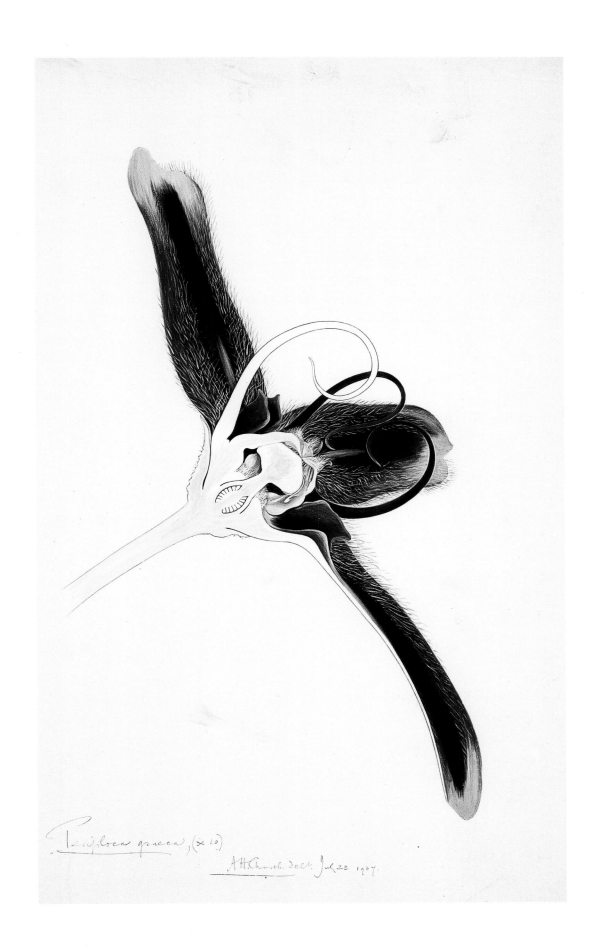

Periploca graeca, (x 10)

A.H.Church. del. Jul 23 1907.

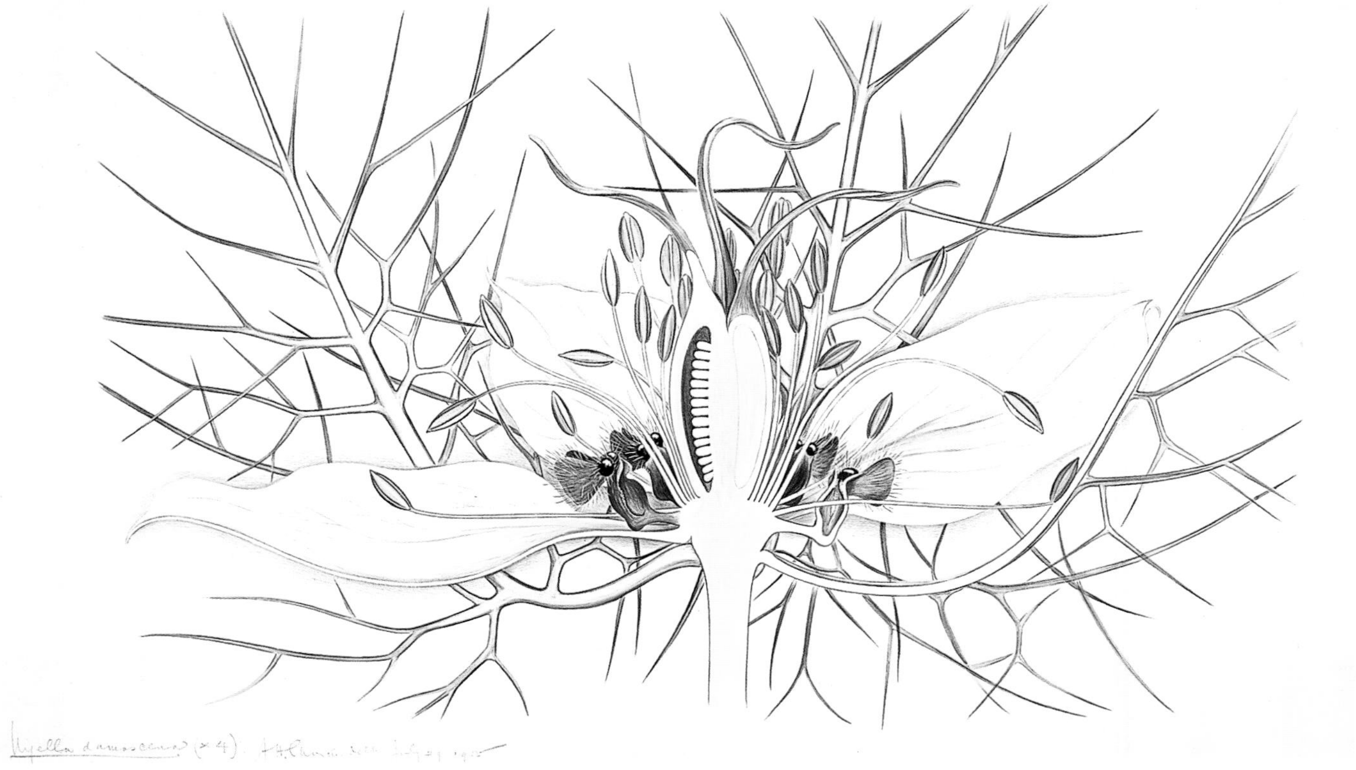

PLATE 41 Love-in-a-mist *Nigella damascena* L. (Ranunculaceae). 29 July 1905. The two-lipped petals have hollow nectariferous claws. Introduced to England from southern Europe *c.* 1570, it was not called love-in-a-mist (or love-in-a-puzzle) until the early nineteenth century. *Nigellus* = blackish, referring to the seeds – those of *N. sativa* L. are the *kalanji* or black cumin of the kitchen, used to flavour nan bread; *damascenus* = from Damascus.

PLATE 42 Policeman's helmet *Impatiens glandulifera* Royle [I. Roylei] (Balsaminaceae). 29 July 1903. Introduced to Britain from the Himalayas in 1839, this balsam had escaped by 1855; it is also naturalized in North America. Like the buddleia *Buddleja davidii* Franchet (Buddlejaceae), introduced in the 1890s from China, this exotic plant is very attractive to the native pollinating fauna. The flowers are visited by bumble bees and completely enclose one when inside, bringing its back in touch with the stigma and stamens in the roof.* In Oxfordshire it was first recorded as escaped in 1911, but by 1927 it was still only in two localities;† now, however over much of England it is a serious pest, particularly along riverbanks, where its fast-growing sappy stems can shade out native plants. The fruit, which explodes violently, dispersing the seeds (hence the generic name), is edible.‡

working on a large book on British seaweeds, apparently to have been produced by Cambridge University Press. By the end of 1919 he had

"done about *2 vols* on Brown , Red algae & 100 pages on Chara, & 200 on Brown flagellates full of beautiful things & they wanted me to sign an agreement for £20 for the lot. So I said I was not taking any! and we have left it at that. Hence I am considering doing the whole show myself. If I can only get the money together to *start*, the Oxford press would do it all right, but it would have to be paid (so far). Then there is all the bother about *pictures* that is why just at present I am sticking to *essays* with *no* pictures."[57]

Eventually some of the bones of this became a *Memoir*. Meanwhile, *Oxford Botanical Memoirs* 4 and 5 appeared: they were based on Church's 22-lecture course, with associated practical work for forestry students, and a major part of the syllabus for the preliminary examination in botany. Appended was his lament 'MINIMUM BOTANY' (*Memoir* 5, p. 23), which is as valid today as it was then:

"Experience of the teaching of elementary Botany in the University during the last decades suggests that there is only one aspect of the subject which has proved of general interest to students and university authorities alike, this being the reduction of such an introductory course to the barest minimum. ... That Botany should be described as the most neglected of modern sciences may be possibly the expression of the incomplete vision of botanists; yet out of a total annual aggregate of about 3000 students in recent years, not more than 1–3 per cent. (and more often 1 than 3) have attended even elementary botanical courses; the great majority of these again only under the compulsion of an examination-system. The subject is practically ignored by classical and literary circles, and equally so by chemists and physicists; while the elementary course may be said to be merely vestigial in Medicine, as recapitulatory of a phase of Herbalism and Pharmacy. At this time of the world's history, it is remarkable that in a university of primary importance, the teaching of Plant-biology should be of such a meagre description.

The fundamental laws of all living organism, including extensions to sociology and theology, are based on biological problems; and biology, or a knowledge of the laws of life, in some form, should be part of the mental equipment of every educated person. It is again Botany, as dealing with the primary life of the world – the great independent kingdom of autotrophic vegetation, the base of the pyramid of life, whether in the sea or on the land, and on which we ourselves as animals are still dependent for our supplies of food and energy – that one must look, not only for the interpretation of the primary laws of existence, but also for the broader views rendered possible by the wider range of plant-races, as expressed for example in the elementary mechanism of phyletic progression."

He prepared a *Memoir* on phyllotaxis, to be number 6, *On the interpretation of the phenomena of phyllotaxis* (1920, 3s. 6d.)[58], explaining to Gepp:

"Doing 'phyllotaxis' has always stamped a man a crank & it makes me acquainted with strange bedfellows. You will find the whole story in T.A. [Sir Theodore] Cook's 'Curves of Life' (I did the phyllotaxis part as you will see by the picture!). Cook was editor of the 'Field' & is a chum of Ray Lankester's. ... I have all but finished of all I want to say (ever) about Phyllotaxis."[59]

After examining it very thoroughly, Church rejected the straight mathematical interpretation of the phenomenon, and this caused him to be heavily criticized by D'Arcy Thompson (1860–1948) in editions of his highly influential *On growth and form* (1st edn, 1917). But modern workers have restored Church's work to its rightful place after 'decades of neglect', and R.V. Jean, the author of the definitive recent work *Phyllotaxis: a systemic study in plant morphogenesis* (1994), dedicated his book to Church.

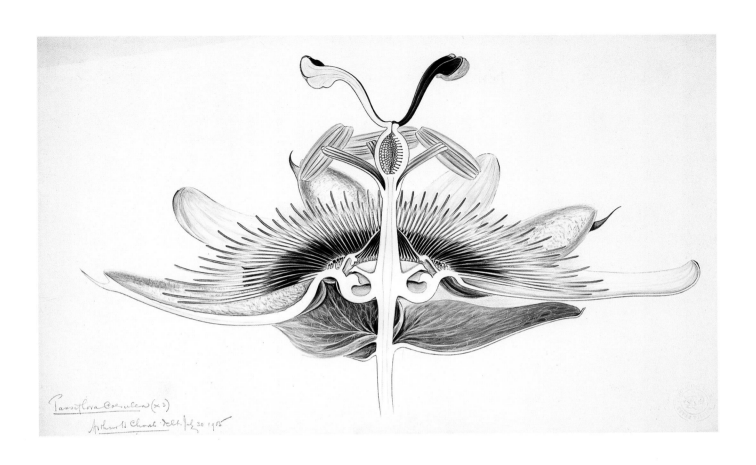

Passiflora Coerulea (×3)
Arthur H Church del. July 30 1905

PLATE 43 Blue passion flower *Passiflora caerulea* L. (Passifloraceae). 30 July 1905.* Native to Brazil and Argentina, this is the hardiest passion flower. *Passiflora, i.e.* Passion flower, refers to the 'Calvary Lesson' of Catholic missionaries in South America, the three styles being the nails on Christ's cross, the five stamens the wounds, the fringe-like corona the crown of thorns, the ten petals and sepals the apostles less Judas Iscariot and Peter, while the lobed leaves and tendrils represent the hands and scourges of Christ's persecutors;† *caerulea* = dark blue.

NOTES

1 *Report of the curators of the Botanic Garden for 1910*, pp. 6–7.

2 *Report of the curators of the Botanic Garden for 1912*, p. 6.

3 Mabberley (2000), p. 754.

4 *Philosophical Transactions of the Royal Society* B, 205, 1914, pp. 115–51, tt. 9–13.

5 Originals preserved in Sherard MS 406 (Department of Plant Sciences, University of Oxford); see Mabberley (1981), p. 249.

6 Harry Champion to Church, 14 April 1915 (Church MSS).

7 *Report of the curators of the Botanic Garden for 1918*, p. 3.

8 Oxford University Archives UR 3/1/18/1, *Registrum scholarum in scientia naturali for 1864–1924*.

9 J.M. Winter, 'Oxford and the First World War', *The History of the University of Oxford, 8: The twentieth century*, ed. B. Harrison, Oxford (Oxford University Press) 1994, pp. 3–25.

10 Death Certificate, 27 January 1916.

11 Section B2 No. 251 (R. Higton *in litt.*, 16 February 2000).

12 Perhaps named after her mother's aunt (see family tree in family's possession).

13 Tansley (1937/8).

14 *Dictionary of national biography.*

15 J.M. Winter, 'Oxford and the First World War', *The History of the University of Oxford, 8: The twentieth century*, ed. B. Harrison, Oxford (Oxford University Press) 1994, pp. 19–21.

16 Church to Gepp, 16 July 1919 (Church MSS).

17 Reprinted in Mabberley (1981), pp. 9–35.

18 p. 27 (Mabberley (1981), p. 35).

19 *Journal of Botany*, 57, 1919, pp. 288–90.

20 *Nature*, 104, 1920, p. 594.

21 *Journal of Botany*, 58, 1920, p. 181

22 See Mabberley (1981), pp. 247–48 for bibliography.

23 Church to Gepp, 18 April 1920 (Church MSS).

24 Church to Gepp, 27 July 1919 (Church MSS).

25 Church to Britten, 2 January 1920 [copy] (Church MSS).

26 Morrell (1997), p. 235.

27 Church to Britten, 2 January 1920 [copy] (Church MSS).

28 Church to Britten, 16 April 1920 [copy] (Church MSS).

29 Church to Gepp, 30 September 1920 (Church MSS).

30 Church to Gepp, 27 July 1919 (Church MSS).

31 Church to Gepp, 14 September 1919 (Church MSS).

32 Church to Gepp, 14 September 1919 (Church MSS).

33 Church to Gepp, 16 July 1919 (Church MSS).

34 Church to Gepp, 31 August 1919 (Church MSS).

35 Church to Gepp, 14 September 1919 (Church MSS).

36 Church to Gepp, 31 August 1919 (Church MSS).

37 Reprinted by Hafner (New York, 1968) and in Mabberley (1981), pp. 37–131.

38 Church to Gepp, 9 October 1919 (Church MSS).

39 Church to Gepp, 9 October 1919 (Church MSS).

40 Church to Gepp, 9 October 1919 (Church MSS).

41 Church to Gepp, 3 November 1919 (Church MSS).

42 Church to Gepp, 6 November 1919 (Church MSS).

43 *Journal of Botany*, 58, 1920, pp. 59–61.

44 *New Phytologist*, 19, 1920, pp. 1–10.

45 Church to Gepp, 9 November 1919 (Church MSS).

46 Church to Gepp, 24 November 1919 (Church MSS).

47 Church to Jackson, 3 November 1919 (Linnean Society Archives).

48 Church to Britten, 2 January 1920 [copy] (Church MSS).

49 *Nature*, 104, 1920, p. 624; see also Boney (1999).

50 Church to Britten, 2 January 1920 [copy] (Church MSS).

51 Church to Gepp, 2 March 1920 (Church MSS).

52 Church to Gepp, 9 November 1919 (Church MSS).

53 See p. 98.

54 Church to Britten, 2 January 1920 [copy] (Church MSS).

55 Church to Gepp, 9 November 1919 (Church MSS).

56 Church to Britten, 16 April 1920 [copy] (Church MSS).

57 Church to Gepp, 9 October 1919 (Church MSS).

58 Reprinted by Hafner (New York, 1968).

59 Church to Gepp, 6 and 7 January 1920 (Church MSS); see Cook, *The curves of life*, 1914, figs. 145, 146, 163, 164, 387, 388.

31 *Gloria dei*. Pencil drawing by A.H. Church (Church MSS II.2 (a) (vii), Bodleian Library, University of Oxford).

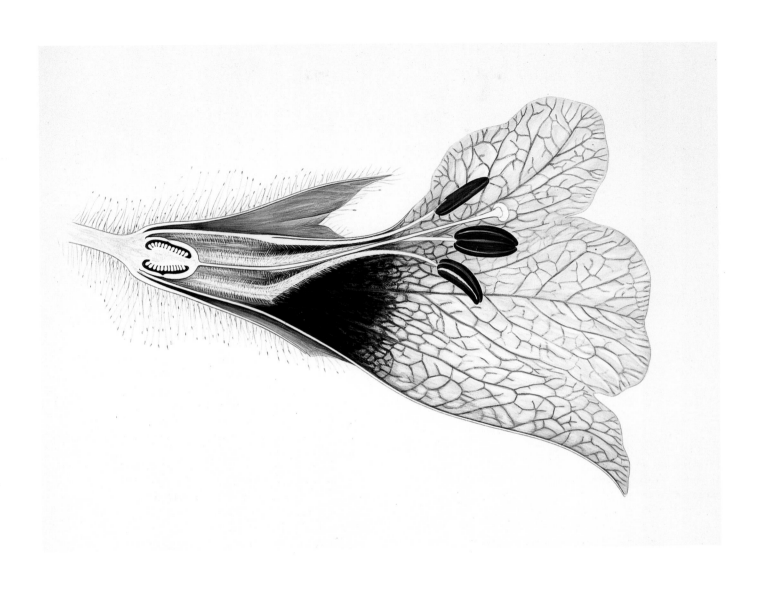

PLATE 44 Henbane *Hyoscyamus niger* L. (Solanaceae). August 1903. Native to temperate Eurasia, henbane has been introduced to North America; seeds can lie dormant for at least a century.* It contains highly toxic alkaloids for which it has been grown commercially; hyoscine was one of the poisons used by Dr Crippen in killing his wife in 1910.† The Assyrians appreciated its efficacy in the treatment of toothache, for which the leaves are still smoked in rural England.‡ *Hyoscyamus* is the Greek name for the plant; *niger* = black.

'The Botany of the Garden in Eden'

32 Professor Sir Arthur Tansley, FRS (1871–1955).

PLATE 45 Bittersweet *Solanum dulcamara* L. (Solanaceae). 2 August 1903. Bittersweet is a common scrambler in hedgerows in Europe and western Asia: it is naturalized in North America and was formerly of some medicinal use; in the Cotswolds the berries, preserved in bottles, are still used to treat chilblains.* *Solanum* flowers have 'buzz' pollination. Here bees hang from the cone formed by the anthers and shiver their indirect flight muscles, which ('buzz') vibration promotes the expulsion from the tips of the anthers of clouds of pollen grains over the insects; this system is known in about 6-8% of angiosperms and is represented in seventy-one plant families with poricidal anthers.† *Solanum* is the Latin name for *S. nigrum* L, black nightshade, some forms of which are used as potherbs, others grown for their fruit used in pies; *dulcis* = sweet, *amara* = bitter, a reference to the fruits, which are intensely bitter, with a sweet aftertaste (not recommended).

"The most majestic productions of the vegetable kingdom are rapidly disappearing, and will never be replaced. No future scheme of forest-cultivation will even countenance a tree growing to maturity in 500–1,000 years, and persisting for 3,000–4,000. The records of an older generation are already often regarded with scepticism. ... Modern forestry prefers a tree of 2 ft. diam. in 100 years."

A.H. Church, *Form-factors in Coniferae*, 3 (1920), n. 4

Church prepared more synopses of his lectures for students, and, in June 1919, could send a set to the Linnean Society: *Elementary notes on gymnosperms and angisperms with special reference to forest-types*, constituting "the rough draft of a textbook, adapted to the special circumstances of teaching at the Oxford Botanic Garden ... a presentation of the subject rather different from that of the hack text-book".[1] The projected book never appeared, but the *Elementary notes* were based on the fifty lectures timetabled that year and some no doubt were those modified for later *Memoirs*. Number 7 was *Elementary notes on the morphology of fungi*, based on thirteen lectures, and it appeared in 1920 (price 2s.), as did numbers 8 and 9, *Elementary notes on conifers*, fifteen lecture and laboratory schedules (2s.), and *Form-factors in Coniferae* (2s.). They are in Church's characteristically dense style, a style that did not please everyone. George Boulger (1853–1922) reviewed the conifer memoirs in the *Journal of Botany*: "such language suggests the description of a man of science as 'one as calls an 'ole a horifice'".[2]

Much in the conifer memoirs was based on new work, using fresh material, including cones of *Cedrus libani* from St John's College garden[3] and pines from Gepp,[4] but also wild material, because, during the War, Church had been able to correspond with Harry Champion, later professor of forestry at Oxford,[5] who collected for him in the United States. Champion, who got firsts in chemistry (1912) and botany (1913) and took the diploma in forestry in 1914, won a Carnegie travelling scholarship in forest entomology for 1914–15, which he took up before join-

33 Harry Champion in the United States (Church MSS).

evolution of maize. Church argued that teosinte was the archaic form of maize, a conclusion now endorsed by both archaeologists and geneticists but until recently vociferously reviled by cytologists, who favoured complicated schemes of intergeneric hybridization to fit their own theories.[9] The importance of human beings in plant-evolution, and the converse, became to grip him. This was manifest first in his interpretation of human history and then in his preoccupation with the importance of humans in the shaping of the British landscape.

Post-war Oxford was flooded with ex-servicemen anxious to be taught. Church captured their imagination by bringing wartime experience to bear on botany. He wrote to Gepp, "I have a long paper on the Botany of the Garden in Eden which always excites people."[10] Unpublished in Church's lifetime, it was printed in 1981[11] and begins in characteristically Churchian prose:

"One of the curious sidelights of the recent war has been the prominence attached to the Mesopotamia Expedition, bringing home to many who never thought about it before the terrible limitations of the climate of the Euphrates Valley and delta, a desert of heat, sand, and flies in the hot season and a pestilential swamp in the wet one; and yet we know that given satisfactory irrigation this region produced the first great civilization of the world of which anything is known, progressing westward as a development which parallels the rise of the oriental nations of the Pacific coast, and, incidentally, the parent-stock of our own social organization. From this ancient civilization we inherit the folklore of still more ancient races, enshrined in myths, which seen through the distorted imagination of the ages survive in the early chapters of the Bible as the story of the

ing the Indian forest service. Champion was one of Church's favourite pupils and his letters to Church from America survive.[6] Champion sent him fresh material of ginkgo and also *Taxodium* for the conifer work[7] but after Church's courses was not impressed with much of the teaching in America: "the average Am. Univ. is a high grade high-school where they practise spoon-feeding."[8]

Through Champion, Church began to correspond with Theodore Cockerell (1866–1948), working in Colorado, on the origin of the sunflower and also the

PLATE 46 Sweet pea *Lathyrus odoratus* L. (Leguminosae). 3 August 1903. Native to southern Italy and Sicily, the sweet pea was first bought to England in 1699. Though the ancestral sweet pea would undoubtedly have been cross-pollinated by bees, all those in cultivation are regularly 'selfed'. There are very many self-pollinated cultivars, some with much reduced scent levels. In the Edwardian period they were the buttonhole and cut flowers *par excellence*. Today most 'sweet pea' soap *etc.* has artificial scent. *Lathyros* is Greek for a pea or pulse; *odoratus* = scented.

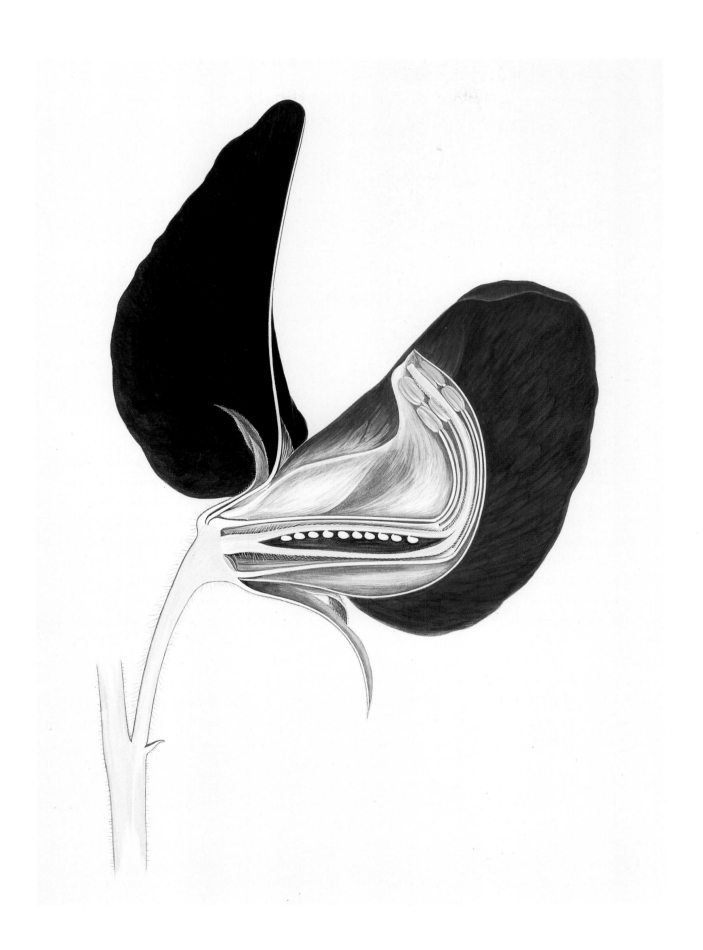

Creation and the Fall, in which these old people groping after their first causes attempted to trace the origin of human life with the means at their disposal. … The story of the Garden of Eden is fundamentally a tale of vegetation and plant-life; it then falls naturally within the province of the botanist."

In analysing "And the Lord planted a garden eastward in Eden" (Genesis 2:8), Church argues the "the Lord" is natural selection and the "garden" the lushness of tropical forest, while the "eastward" points to India, in other words, "natural selection evolved a jungle east of Babylon."

"The story of the Garden of Eden is to begin with, therefore, a folk myth of Sumerian migrants lost in the Euphrates valley who treasured dreams of a golden age in their history when their happy ancestors lived under conditions wholly different … in a tropical jungle, a naked arboreal race, fruit-eating and happy-go-lucky according to their tradition, to whom work of any sort was unknown. …

Adam turns out to be a little brown man of the jungle … two terrors of the jungle remain deeply impressed in the constitution of the race and relics of them persist till today, even in this country in which they are practically unknown."

And he goes on to explain the familiar concern over poisonous berries and the terror of snakes, which he tracks back to the strychnine-filled *Strychnos nux-vomica* and the king cobra of India, both to be found in Genesis as the forbidden fruit and the serpent.

"The Fall is merely a very plausible method of accounting for the existence of the tribe under its new conditions of hardship … the later phases of the story are as vivid as the first; for some reason or other beyond their comprehension, and therefore to be plausibly explained, the tribe are driven out of the forest land to a semi-desert full of xerophytic vegetation, actually expressed as thorns and thistles, exposed to brilliant sun, necessitating some sort of clothing. Lastly we have the dire consequences, the curse of creation, of man, of woman, and the snake, all seen through the jaundiced eyes of toiling humanity, filled again with an egotism, which still prevails, that all creation was solely made to minister to man's needs."

Church was still absorbed with the consequences of his *Thalassiophyta* ideas not only with respect to extant seaweeds but also to the evolution of lichens. He told Gepp, "The lichen fungus is the old seaweed itself", and he was reworking his material for the Cambridge seaweed book as a *Memoir*. "I am trying to get a few jokes into the next

PLATE 47 *Fuchsia magellanica* Lam. 'Riccartonii' [F. Riccartoni] (Onagraceae). 18 August 1910. *Fuchsia magellanica* is native to southern South America, though this cultivar is possibly of hybrid origin. This bushy fuchsia is planted as hedging in western Britain and Ireland, and is characteristic of the countryside of the Isle of Man; it is an aggressive weed in other parts of the world, notably Hawaii, where it invades the native forest on some islands.* The pendulous fleshy flowers are bird-pollinated: the flower-stalk is flexible so that if a bird probes too hard the flower is pushed aside, escaping damage, while attempts to puncture the corolla to get nectar are frustrated.† The berries are edible. Linnaeus named *Fuchsia* after Leonhard Fuchs, for whom Church had enormous respect. He wrote "The original standard for all subsequent volumes of illustrations of plants was set up by the genius of one man, Leonard [sic] Fuchs (1501–1566), a leading physician and professor of his time, a wealthy man of considerable influence and with great insight into the scientific needs of his day. His volume 'DE HISTORIA STIRPIUM', published at Basle (1542), is generally recognized as the starting-point of floristic work, in addition to its significance as a compendium of the 'Virtues of Herbs'" ('Brunfels and Fuchs', *Journal of Botany*, 57, 1919, p. 233). The specific name refers to the Straits of Magellan.

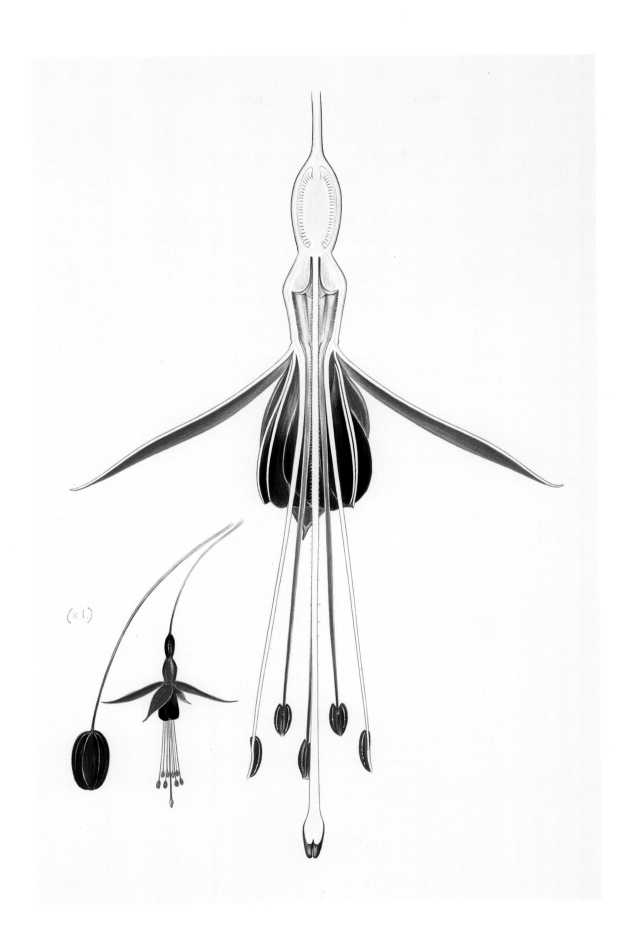

(×1.)

algal paper to keep it from being too dry before getting finally quit of it. But I think you will see it fills a vast gap in Botany, all the story of the evolution of the Leaf and Root & such things put down quite simply at last & not swallowed as 'Morphology' cut & dried & purely academic."[12] He sent Gepp what had become *Memoir 10, The somatic organization of the Phaeophyceae* (1920, 5s.) early in 1921, commenting "I rather like the new white paper even if it is much thinner & keeps the part from looking *too* big a job to tackle!"[13] In it he outlined the construction of marine plants effectively 'pre-adapting' them to life on land, the bridge between the *Autotrophic flagellate* and *Thalassiophyta* and thus completing his great trilogy. In his summary he wrote:

"The plant-soma of the land is but the seaweed soma adapted and 'enlarged' for its new conditions. The general features of habit still traced in a forest-tree were laid down, once for all, in the first benthic filaments of the rising sea-bottom. Later details may change, but the fundamental features ingrained by primal natural selection are not affected. So long as the general mechanism of life runs on similar biological lines of autotrophy, the mechanism evolved as the response to one phase may serve sufficiently well for the biological problems of a new one; if it does not, it may be modified. But there is no known mechanism in living organism for starting again *de novo* from nothing at all. There must be something in hand as equipment to build on; and just what the land-plant has been built on is determined by what is found in the sea.

The general trend of botanical teaching of the last generation appears to have followed the principle of taking care of the reproductive processes and the soma will look after itself. Comparative morphology has been allowed to deteriorate to a vanishing point; the word 'morphology' being transferred to considerations of the gametophytes, the sexual organs, or the sporogenous tissue of land-flora. The mental outlook of a school which can conceive a gigantic forest-tree as the mere outcome of an intercalated post-sexual phase, as presented in the feeblest organisms of the land, evolved in comparatively recent times (from the horizon of the Lower Devonian), finds no difficulty whatever in discussing the progression of somatic specialization and is as much beyond argument as it fails to attract the student. Such minor details as stems, leaves, and roots, with their complex structural factors, appear to come by nature, just as to older morphologists any photosynthetic structure must sooner or later present 'leaf' characters. Given a moss capsule, the timber-tree follows as a minor detail, so long as it produces asexual tetrads."

In this he was tilting at Bower and the establishment: in time, as we have seen, his 'jokes' would backfire.

In the spring of 1920

"A man turned up from Portugal bringing me back some orchids, all of these just going over. So I had to drop everything to get them drawn: & it took me 6 days. He brought me species of Ophrys, always a pet theory of mine. But by the time I had drawn each twice over, I began to see I had nearly all I wanted — for the theory of the Ophrys flower. It will make a nice Memoir when I can get the money for some coloured plates!! and I have got hold of the meaning of the thing which has stumped me for years. The paper will be called *Floral Camouflage. … O. speculum* is a beautiful thing, the most perfect copy of a fly ever seen with *metallic blue* abdomen."[14]

PLATE 48 *Psychopsis papilio* (Lindl.) H. Jones [Oncidium papilio] (Orchidaceae). 20 August 1912. Four tropical American orchid species formerly included in the very large genus *Oncidium* comprise the genus *Psychopsis*. *P. papilio* is native from Peru to Trinidad and was introduced to cultivation in Britain by the governor of Trinidad, Sir Ralph Woodward. The generic name comes from the Greek *psyche*, butterfly and —*opsis*, appearance; *papilio* is Latin, also for butterfly!

Oncidium papilio
Krameranium. (x2)

A.H.Church delt. Aug 20 1912

He explained to Gepp that he

"… had to go out & buy a new set of paints & get into the swing of painting again. It was a useful job. I haven't drawn a flower for 5 years & thought I never should again, but I have got the machine in running order & invented a new style of figure, which is more within my range. My eyes won't do the fine work I used to any more, so I have to get hold of a coarse method that will stand reduction." [15]

He continued work on the project, drawing British species of *Ophrys* until at least 1928.[16]

In 1920 Church was proposed for a fellowship of the Royal Society, "distinguished as a botanist with wide interests". His sponsors were Seward, Scott, Vines, Sir Isaac Balfour (1853–1922), formerly Sherardian professor and later Regius Keeper of the Royal Botanic Garden Edinburgh, and Vernon H. Blackman (1872–1967), professor of plant physiology and pathology at Imperial College, but he was not elected until the following year, when the list was strengthened by the addition of Frederick Weiss (1865–1953), professor of botany at Manchester University, Poulton and Keeble.[17] In explaining his honour to Annie Lorrain Smith (1854–1937), the lichenologist at The Natural History Museum, Church added, "I write to congratulate Mr Britten on his valuable tuition, since I sent him the first '[Magnus] Spence [1853–1919]' paper [on Orcadian seaweeds, published in the *Journal of Botany* 56, 1918, pp. 281–85, 338–40] & started on a career of verbosity."[18]

By April 1920 Church was finding his workload oppressive, lecturing each day then frantically writing the next day's lectures immediately afterwards, "I have 5 hours teaching on Friday & after that to get up to lec-

34 Pencil sketch for watercolour opposite (Church MSS, 'Floral mimicry').

ture on Saturday, so one is more or less like a limp rag at the end. I find 2 hours continuous talking quite enough, now."[19] While Sir William Schlich FRS (1840–1925) was professor of forestry, there was a diploma in forestry with large numbers of candidates: thirty-six in 1920 for example, including Captain Henry Blunt (born 1889), who was to become a forester in the

PLATE 49 *Ophrys speculum* Link (Orchidaceae). Watercolour by Arthur Harry Church. 9 April 1920 (Church MSS, 'Floral mimicry'). Pollinated by male scoliid wasps, *Camposcolia ciliata*, which emerge before females. They are not attracted if the lip is cut off: it seems to produce scent stimulants besides a colour strongly reminiscent of the females; in attempting to mate with the flowers, the act of pseudocopulation, the males remove pollinia and take them to a second flower effecting cross-pollination during a second pseudocopulatory attempt.*

Ophrys is a Greek name for a plant (unidentified) with two leaves; *speculum* = mirror, an allusion to the shiny lip.

Sudan and later to acquire many of Church's photographic plates.[20] Of the fifty-three to be awarded the diploma in 1921, Lawrence Chalk (1895–1979), later co-author (with C.R. Metcalfe) of the monumental *Anatomy of Dicotyledons* (1950), was awarded a distinction.

By 1921 Church was giving 135 lectures a year, while Keeble was giving 124, loads unthinkable today.[21] In 1923 the old forestry diploma was abolished and a new graduate one initiated, so that from the dozens previously awarded there were now only one or two a year. Conditions at the Botanic Garden were very cramped and there was no electricity there until 1921,[22] but in 1923 Magdalen College closed its laboratory there and part of it became research rooms for the department.[23]

From 1921 onwards, those reading for final honours in botany resumed pre-war levels. Those taught by Church included: George Robert ['Robin'] S. Snow (1897–1962; first class, 1921), who took up the study of phyllotaxis and became a great benefactor to the department after his marriage to Christine Pilkington (first class, 1926), of the glass-manufacturing family; Harry Baker (1895–1958; second class, 1922), who went on to become demonstrator in the department; Mary Chattaway (1899–1997; first class, 1923), the distinguished plant anatomist, who worked with Lawrence Chalk; Leonard Wigg (1900–1980; third class, 1924), later deputy conservator of forests in Tanganyika; Ivan R. Dale (c. 1904–1963; first class, 1927), later a forester in Kenya; Arthur C. Hoyle (1905–1986; first class, 1927), later curator of the Forest Herbarium at Oxford; Edward Yemm (1909–1993; first class, 1931) and the husband of Marie Solari (first class, 1930),[24] later professor of botany at Bristol University, F. Bayard Hora (1908–1984, first class, 1932), later reader in botany at Reading University; and Nicholas Polunin (1908–1997; first class, 1932), later president of the World Council for the Biosphere.[25] Many of these and others were first to take overseas posts in the colonial service.

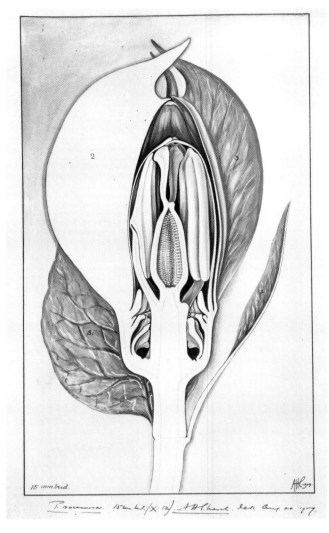

35 *Passiflora racemosa* Brot., vertical section of bud 15 mm long. Unpublished figure for *Types of floral mechanism*, ink and wash on Bristol board, 20 August 1909 (Church MSS).

Apart from the material included in the *Memoirs*, initially intended for his students, all of Church's published output was now submitted to the *Journal of Botany*. His papers on lichens appeared from 1920 to 1921, largely serialized.[26] They not only dealt with their position in his *Thalassiophyta* view of evolution, but also dwelt on

PLATE 50 Red passion flower *Passiflora racemosa* Brot. (Passifloraceae). 21 August 1909. A Brazilian bird-pollinated passion flower, described from a cultivated plant introduced to Lisbon by a Mr Woodman. See plate 43 for origin of the generic name; *racemosa* refers to the structure of the inflorescence, a raceme.

their life-cycles and the nature of the symbiosis between the dominant fungus and the associated algae.

"Lichens thus present an interesting case of an algal race, deteriorating along the lines of a heterotrophic existence, yet arrested, as it were, on the somatic down-grade, by the adoption of intrusive algal units of lower degree to subserve photosynthesis (much in the manner of the marine worm *Convoluta*). Thus arrested, they have been able to retain more definite expression of more deeply inherent factors of these-weed habit and construction than any other race of Fungi."[27]

Then came a series of papers apparently stimulated by Bower's 'Land flora', but again really extensions of *Thalassiophyta*, on reproductive mechanisms and life-cycles and spores, sporogonia, sporangia and sporophylls.[28] Although less tortured in style than his earlier work, they have been neglected and will repay renewed study.

Church wrote to Gepp:

"Also I now have a new sideline in 'water divining'. There is a good local diviner & I am getting him to do really useful work in plotting on a map subterranean springs. We have just followed the best Oxford one from field to field & through hedges & wire for 10 miles as far, that is, as the unaided legs can go without a motor car. It would amuse you to see such mad idiots!"[29]

In 1919 at the Magdalen College laboratory, he had carried out experiments on J. Timms, a professional diviner and member of the well-known local boat-build-

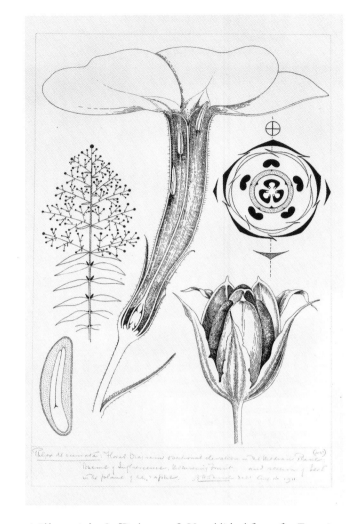

36 *Phlox paniculata* L. [P. decussata]. Unpublished figure for *Types of floral mechanism*, ink on Bristol board, 16 August 1911 (Church MSS). Vertical section of flower, diagram of inflorescence structure, floral diagram, section of seed in the plane of the raphe, dehiscing fruit capsule.

PLATE 51 Phlox *Phlox paniculata* L. [P. decussata] (Polemoniaceae). 30 August 1909. The highly scented perennial garden phlox is native to eastern North America. The flowers are moth-pollinated. Phlox was first grown in Britain by James Sherard (1666–1738) in his garden at Eltham in Surrey in 1732. He was the younger brother of William Sherard (1658/9–1728), who was British consul in what is now Izmir, Turkey, and founded the Sherardian chair, held in Church's time by Vines, Keeble and Tansley. Today over 100 cultivars of phlox are offered by the trade. *Phlox* is Greek for a flame-coloured flower, in classical times used for certain *Silene* species; *paniculata* refers to the branching system in the inflorescence.

ing family: the results were "entirely successful". Despite his sceptical outlook on life in general, Church was impressed and wrote to the *Oxford Times*,[30] though in January 1921 a piece printed there was entitled "Intuition an aid to water divining": Timms "merely carried out with a divining rod the way of the springs that his instinct and intuition had already told him before leaving home".[31]

Timms was accompanied by "Dr Russell, tutor of science at Christ Church & editor of 'Discovery', who represented Science and the University, while the Mayor and several Councillors represented the City". Timms used traditional hazel twigs, leading his party from one end of the city to the other. Then further laboratory tests were tried: "Mr Timms is not confined to one particular kind of wooden prong, and is particularly senstitive to metal. He responds to nickel, gold, silver, and copper in decreasing order." From January to June 1921 Church helped Timms to plot the course of Oxford's underground streams, accompanying him on outing after outing, but experiments carried out in the Clarendon Laboratory under the auspices of the formidable Professor Frederick Lindemann (1886–1957), later Lord Cherwell and Churchill's adviser, did not work and Church seems to have lost interest.

But getting around the Oxford district, particularly with Harry Baker, led Church to put together what would now be described as an ecological survey of the region. He had been teaching 'oecology' since at least 1909,[32] and in 1920 let Gepp know that "I am going to have a shot at a new 'Flora' of the District"[33] because he found Druce's standard Flora of the county "useless" for teaching.[34] By April 1921 he could report:

"Just at present we are doing a 'flora' stunt in the fine weather & trying to see what can be really made out of the flora for teaching purposes. I have just struck [on] the idea of an 'Ecological' Flora as opposed to a 'collector's' flora of the district, the former being only ½ the number of plants in the latter. The definition is that when the number of individuals of the species is less than the number of collectors in a given area, the species ceases to be ecologically interesting (or important). In my spare time I am taking a lot of photos to illustrate it."[35]

He was helped by students as well as by Baker, who seems to have been his constant companion in the field. By September 1921 he could tell Gepp, "I have all the introductory chapters roughed out."[36]

At the same time Church was bringing out yet more schedules as *Memoirs*: *Elementary notes on the systematy of angiosperms* (no. 11, 1921, 3s. 6d.) and *Introduction to the systematy of Indian trees* (no. 12, 1921, 2s. 6d.); of the latter he wrote that "however imperfect, [it] may serve as the beginning of a more definitive modern course of Tropical Botany".[37] In October 1921 he had "no less than 6 more memoirs more or less in hand",[38] but only three more *Memoirs* were to be published, all of them the results of the 'Flora' work.

Oxford Botanical Memoirs 13–15 (1922–25) were called *Introduction to the plant-life of the Oxford district* and were illustrated with Church's own photographs. In typical style the first ('General review – 1922', 3s. 6d) begins

"Once free from streets and houses, considered as mere evidence of the gregarious habits of a modern

PLATE 52 Foxglove *Digitalis purpurea* L. (Scrophulariaceae). 1 September 1905. Native throughout western Europe, it was formerly the source of the heart drug, digitalis, publicized by William Withering in his *An acount of the foxglove* (1785). During the First World War the minute seeds were collected by children in southern England for processing for medicinal use, as part of the 'war effort'.* Today, though, the principal agent of digitalis, digoxin, is largely extracted from *Digitalis lanata* Ehrh. of central Europe, grown commercially in The Netherlands.† The flowers produce a lot of nectar and are pollinated by bees; the hairs in the lower part of the flower provide footholds for the bees, whose backs come into contact with the stamens and stigma in the roof of the flower.

Digitalis in Latin means a finger's breadth, referring to the flower-size; *purpurea* = purple.

37 Oxford from the seven-field footpath, South Hinksey with 'Yeoman' wheat at harvest, 7 August 1923 (Church MSS). Reproduced in *Oxford Botanical Memoirs* 15, frontispiece). A greatly enlarged print of this celebrated photograph graced the windows of a photographer's shop in the High Street, Oxford, for many years.*

population with the quite natural obsession that the world was specially designed for the welfare of the human race, it is only necessary to take an unbiased view of the condition of the surrounding country, to be inevitably inclined to the conclusion that, even in this part of the world, where half the year is spent in a struggle with the cold and storms of winter, *Plant-life is enormously preponderant*, and the vegetation of the countryside is the primary phase of life to be considered in dealing with all biological problems of the locality.

Trees or grass clothe the visible surface of the land, in close canopy or as thick undergrowth; animal life, beyond a few birds and the animals maintained by man, is conspicuously inconspicuous. Towns appear but as ant-heaps spaced far apart in the general green mantle of vegetation; and however much man may interfere with and attempt to dominate or even to replace the indigenous flora, his attempts are of doubtful permanence. ... The local Oxford flora can show no heath-moors, alpine slopes, sand-dunes, shingle beaches or estuarine swamps, which have so attracted ecologists in other directions [a dig at Tansley]; it remains characteristically commonplace, sylvestral, agrestal, paludal, with no special developments in any direction, and with little to attract the visitor from other more favoured districts.

Yet it is this very commonplace character which constitutes its greatest asset. With attention no longer distracted by special factors or extreme conditions of soil or water-supply, one may settle down to the examination of just what constitutes the ordinary flora of the river-valleys of the central plain of England. ... The floras of other more emphasized biological districts are equally commonplace to the natives of those regions, and the plants of an English countryside may have a special scientific interest alike for the inhabitants of Greenland's icy mountains or those of India's coral strand, as conversely the English botanist is expected to be familiar with the ecology of those distant lands. To a floating population of students, the analysis of the local flora may serve as a guide to the methods of attacking the general problems of plant-life quite as well as any other. Though it may be characterized as 'homely' in its general features, it is nevertheless essentially British and English in its more fundamental factors. In spite of modern tendencies for admiring any country but one's own, it must be remembered that for all those who in this country are still privileged to trace an Anglo-Saxon origin, plant-life of this description has been intimately associated with the life of the essentially English race for a period of some 50 generations (1,500 years)."[39]

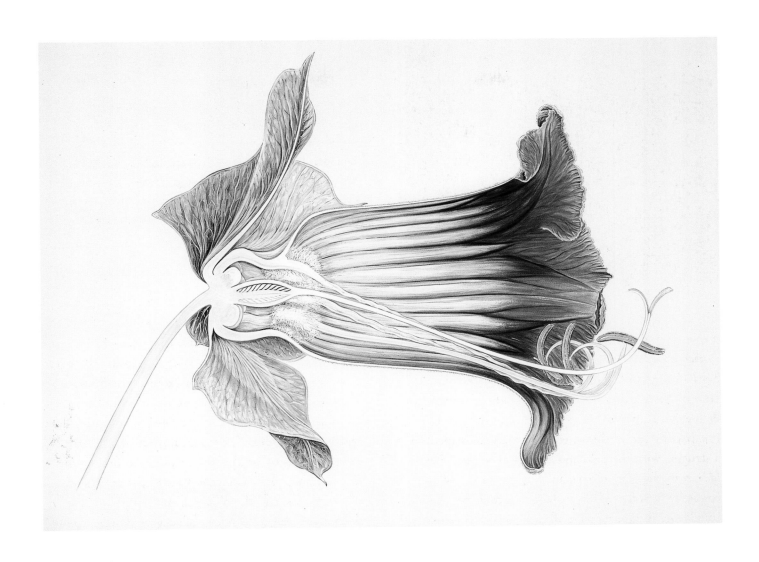

PLATE 53 *Cobaea scandens* Cav. (Polemoniaceae). 2 September 1909. Introduced in 1787, *Cobaea scandens* is native to Mexico but widely naturalized, especially in the neo-tropics. It is a liane and can grow to 8 m in a season in Britain. The flowers are protandrous, at first greenish-cream with an unpleasant smell, when they are visited by flies;* later they become purplish with a pleasant honey-smell with much nectar. Although bees visit them then in England, they are probably bat-pollinated in the wild. *Cobaea* commemorates the Jesuit Father, Bernardo Cobo (1572–1659), a Spanish missionary and naturalist working in Mexico and Peru; *scandens* = climbing.

"The **British Flora**, as the deteriorated representative of deciduous forest-land remote from the tropics, affords a wide range of biological stations, woodland, open ground, and aquatic environment. It thus presents a complex in which there is room for something of everything: all biological lines are represented, even if only by one or two forms in an attenuated scheme. It still retains a few evergreen trees, now sub-dominant to the main series of deciduous forest-forms. Underwood trees and shrubs are well represented, with not only an abundant ground-flora, but a few residual representatives of the secondary vegetation of the tropical forest as parasites, epiphytes, saprophytes and liana-climbers."[40]

Church's straightforward analysis of the vegetation from the least to the most modified is so useful that this author found it invaluable as a teaching aid until the 1990s. The first volume ends:

"English gardens, instead of being filled with simples and a few decorative flowers, become the repositories of exotic forms from all parts of the world, their mutants, hybrids, and teratological phenomena, more particularly in the form of 'florist's flowers', as the apotheosis of the alien, assisted and selected by man, in a wholly artificial and arbitrary manner, not invariably directed by the best taste, perception of form, or colour-sense, and usually entirely ignoring the meaning, function, and evolution of the floral and reproductive mechanism. Before these the indigenous flora shrinks as an assemblage of weeds, on no account to be tolerated inside the garden-walls, except

in the form of turf. Where the last interest of such forms centres in the manner in which they may be Mendelized, or inter-crossed to give still more puzzling freaks, one may still turn with relief to the honest free-fighters of the wild, knowing the great strengths such plants have in reserve, and the rapid and devastating manner in which they would return once the hand of man were relaxed. The best gardens are only measured in hundreds of years, the wild flora in hundreds of thousands, the scope of Modern Botany takes into account many hundreds of millions."

The other two volumes deal with the annual succession, January–June (14, 1925, 3s. 6d) and July–December (15, 1925, 3s. 6d.); the latter ends:

"Hence the story repeats in successive years with a precision which at once affords the most mysteriously beautiful feature of the countryside, as it is the most constant factor in determining the main lines of all social organization. In an age which exploits coal and petrol, it is well to remember that human life is still wholly dependent on living plant-plasma, and likely to remain so indefinitely. The world-supply of coal and petrol is, after all, finite, and the plant remains the simplest and cheapest means of obtaining current supplies of solar energy, as well as being the source of essential food-substances beyond the hopes of chemical synthesis."

The eccentric John Fothergill (1876–1957), sometime disciple of Oscar Wilde and by this time gentleman-publican of The Spreadeagle at Thame, near Oxford –

PLATE 54 Nasturtium *Tropaeolum majus* L. (Tropaeolaceae). 3 September 1903. Introduced in 1684 from Peru, the nasturtium is known only in cultivation: the original stock may have been of hybrid origin, the parents being *T. minus* L. and *T. ferreyae* Sparre in the Lima area.* Since then, other species have been bred into garden stocks. The nasturtium was so called because it has mustard-oils, nasturtium being a word used for pungent-tasting plants in general. But today the technical name, *Nasturtium*, is a synonym of *Rorippa*, watercress, of which *R. nasturtium-aquaticum* (L.) Hayek is a common wild species in Europe. *Tropaeolum* comes from *tropaion*, Greek for trophy, the plant climbing a post being redolent of classical trophies of round shields and golden helmets on a pillar, used to mark victories on the battlefield; *majus* = larger, by comparison with *T. minus*, a non-climbing species.

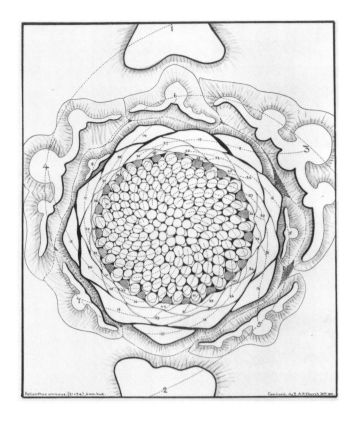

38 Phyllotactic diagram of sunflower bud 6 mm in diameter, drawn using a *camera lucida*, 1901. Unpublished figure for *Types of floral mechanism*, ink and wash on Bristol board (Church MSS), a simpler form of which was published in *On the relation of phyllotaxis to mechanical laws*, Part II, 1902, fig. 50.

a pub where local people were not allowed and with a foyer where Fothergill fed live mice to a black eagle[41] — wrote in his diary in 1928:

"Dr A.H. Church … came the other day to tea with his daughter and now sends me his volume *Succession of Wild Flowers in Oxfordshire* [*Plant-life of the Oxford district*]. In spite of recording his appalling knowledge with the mind of a Blue Book [a parliamentary publication, usually the report of a royal commission or of a committee] writer he has the light green soul of a gardener and with the help of his living photographs the book *is* the countryside; wherever it goes you have your nose on the ground; lawn and water plants, weed heaps and hay fields rush past you in their course from Spring to Winter with their Latin names."[42]

But it was less readily embraced by the ecological establishment. Church's ecological work was set in his evolutionary framework in such a way that an apparently local treatise stretches beyond the narrow confines of plant ecology as it was then understood. His work did

PLATE 55 Sunflower *Helianthus annuus* L. (Compositae); hermaphrodite disk-floret left and upper right, sterile ray-floret and receptacular scale right. 15 September 1909. As with all Compositae, the pollen is released into the tubular floret and pushed out by the extending style (left), here with separating branches (top right). The sunflower was introduced into Europe from North America in 1510; today it is second only to soybean as an oil crop, the seeds being rich in polyunsaturates, especially linoleic acid.* The oil-cake is used as fodder and the husks are used in fuel-logs in Canada. Church was very interested in the origin of he single-headed unbranched annual plant, arguing that it arose from perennial stock with many smaller heads (see p. 92). *Helianthus* is from the Greek *helios*, sun, and *anthos*, flower; *annuus* refers to the annual habit.

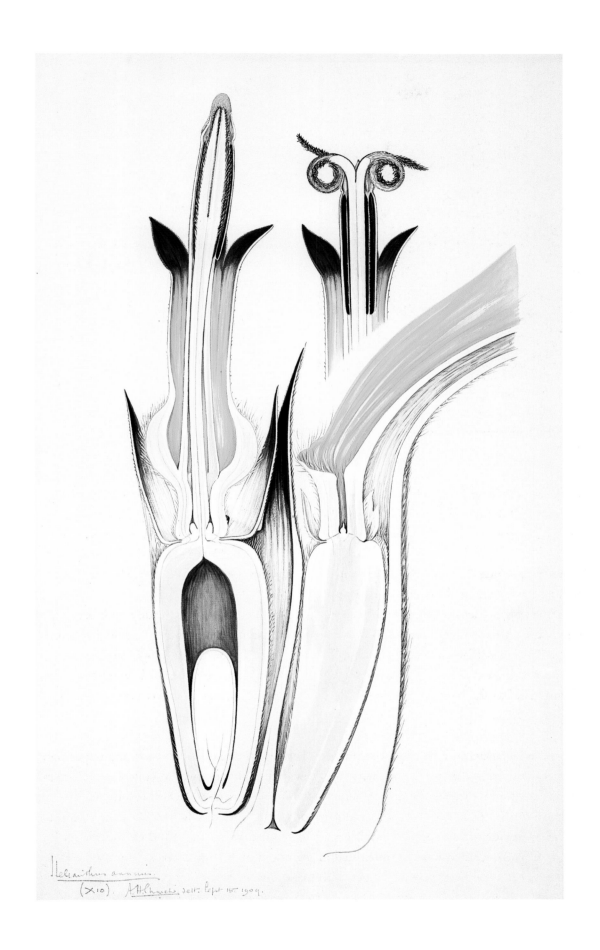

Helianthus annuus.
(×10). A H Church delt. Sept 15 1904.

not pander to the ecological 'systems' fashionable at the time. He did not publish any of his ecological work elsewhere and perhaps the *Memoirs*' apparently parochial contents have led to their being neglected. But there is perhaps more to it than that, because, despite its freshness and bold approach, his work was not to be cited in the standard ecological text in Britain, Arthur Tansley's monumental *British Isles and their vegetation* (1939). As with Bower's summation of botanical progress in the sixty years to 1930, Church was brushed aside.

It was Tansley, the editor of the *Journal of Ecology*, who was to be elected Sherardian professor in succession to Keeble, who resigned the chair for a post at ICI. With few collaborators, Keeble had done next to no research at Oxford and apparently discouraged 'too scientific' an approach to botany. His time at Oxford is scarcely mentioned in the saccharine self-indulgence of his autobiographical effort *Polly and Freddie* (1936). At Boar's Hill, he "indulged in extensive hospitality, groomed himself flamboyantly like a Louis-Philippe courtier, rejoiced in his knighthood (1922) and concentrated on horticulture".[43] Keeble sincerely hoped that his knighthood would help the department, but on his telling Church this, Church retorted, "We will live it down".[44]

The post, with a salary of £1200, was advertised in the *Oxford University Gazette* for 10 November 1926. It has generally been held that Church applied for it, but his name is not on the list of eight candidates for the Sherardian chair,[45] which included William Atkins FRS (1884–1959), physiologist at the Marine Biological Association laboratory at Plymouth (Church was on its council at the time), and the palaeobotanist Hugh

Hamshaw Thomas (1885–1962), and the mycologist Frederick T. Brooks (1882–1952), both from Cambridge. The electors met on 20 January 1927 and chose another Cambridge man from the list, Arthur Tansley, whom Seward had favoured in the previous election.[46]

Tansley was a man of independent means and had resigned his Cambridge lecturership in 1923 to devote himself to Freudian psychology. Once in Oxford, he set about modernizing the department and increasing the teaching staff. In 1925 Church had been reappointed lecturer for five years, but following Tansley's election, he was appointed university demonstrator (a category invented that year) in botany for four years from 1 October 1927 at an annual salary of £750, with a requirement to lecture in every term.[47] He was joined in the same year by William Wilkins (1886–1966), to teach mycology,[48] and in 1928 by William James (1900–1978) to teach plant physiology.

NOTES

1 Church to Linnean Society, 21 June 1919 (Linnean Society Archives).
2 *Journal of Botany*, 59, 1921, pp. 81–82.
3 Church to Gepp, 24 July 1920 (Church MSS).
4 Church to Gepp, 30 September 1920 (Church MSS).
5 F.C. Osmaston, 'Obituary', *Commonwealth Forestry Review*, 58, 1979, pp. 143–44.
6 Church MSS.
7 Champion to Church, 9 December 1914 (Church MSS).
8 Champion to Church, 28 March 1915 (Church MSS).
9 Cf. Mabberley (2000), p. 765.
10 Church to Gepp, 9 October 1919 (Church MSS).
11 Mabberley (1981), pp. 237–45.
12 Church to Gepp, 30 September 1920 (Church MSS).
13 Church to Gepp, 5 January 1921 (Church MSS).

PLATE 56 *Ceropegia linearis* E. Meyer ssp. *woodii* (Schltr.) H. Huber [*C. woodsii*] (Asclepiadaceae/Apocynaceae). 19 September 1905. Native from Zimbabwe to the eastern Cape of South Africa, this slender scrambler is familiar as an accommodating house-plant; it has heart-shaped mottled leaves and aerial tubers borne on the wiry stems. The flowers act as a pollinator-trap: biting midges are attracted by smell, colour and the long apical hairs flickering in the breeze. They are detained below because downward-pointing conical papillae, coated in oil, in the tube prevent their escape.* A day or two later the tube becomes horizontal and the hairs wither so that the midges can escape carrying the pollinia on their proboscides. *Ceropegia* is from the Greek *keros*, wax, and *pege*, fountain, referring to the flowers; *linearis* = narrow; *woodii* commemorates John Medley Wood (1827–1915), curator of the Durban Botanic Garden and discoverer of the plant in Natal in 1881.

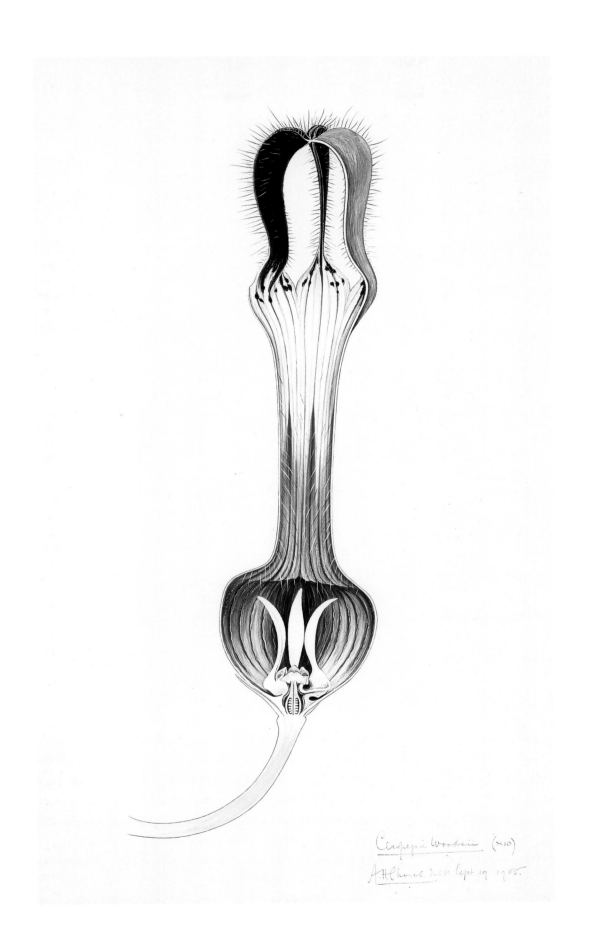

Ceropegia Woodsii (×10)
A.H.Church del. Sept 19 1905.

113

14 Church to Britten, 16 April 1920 [copy] (Church MSS).

15 Church to Gepp, 18 April 1920 (Church MSS).

16 Drawing of 'Early Spider', 19 May 1928 (Church MSS).

17 Royal Society candidacy records.

18 Church to Lorrain Smith, 21 March 1921 [copy] (Church MSS).

19 Church to Gepp, 28 April 1920 (Church MSS).

20 Archives, University of Oxford, FOR/SF/2, *Sussex Life*, 1976, p. 21.

21 *Oxford University Gazette*, 27 April 1921, p. 556.

22 *Oxford University Gazette*, 27 April 1921, p. 556.

23 Morrell (1997), p. 235.

24 Morrell (1997), p. 238.

25 Oxford University Archives, UR 3/1/18/1 & 2, *Registrum scholarum in scientia naturali 1864–1924 and 1925–1950*.

26 See Mabberley (1981), p. 248.

27 *Journal of Botany*, 58, 1920, p. 267.

28 See Mabberley (1981), p. 248.

29 Church to Gepp, 15 January 1921 (Church MSS).

30 'Oxford water 1921', Church MSS III (viii), Bodleian Library, University of Oxford.

31 *Oxford Times*, 9 January 1921.

32 *Oxford University Gazette*, 26 April 1910.

33 Church to Gepp, 7 November 1920 (Church MSS).

34 Church to Britten, 14 September 1921 (Church MSS).

35 Church to Gepp, 18 Apr 1921 (Church MSS).

36 Church to Gepp, 15 sept 1921 (Church MSS).

37 p. 2.

38 Church to Gepp, 17 October 1921 (Church MSS).

39 Reprinted in Mabberley (1981), pp. 133–235.

40 p. 44 (Mabberley, 1981, p. 176).

41 S. Goffe, *Thame past and present*, Zoltbommel (Europen Library) 1998.

42 *An innkeeper's diary*, London (Folio Society), 2000, p. 162.

43 Morrell (1997), p. 236.

44 F.B. Hora *in litt.*, 14 March 1978.

45 Morrell (1997), p. 236.

46 Archives, University of Oxford DC9/1/1 (*teste* Simon Bailey *in litt.*, October 1999).

47 *Oxford University Gazette*, 11 May 1927, p. 543.

48 *Oxford University Gazette*, 15 June 1927, p. 672.

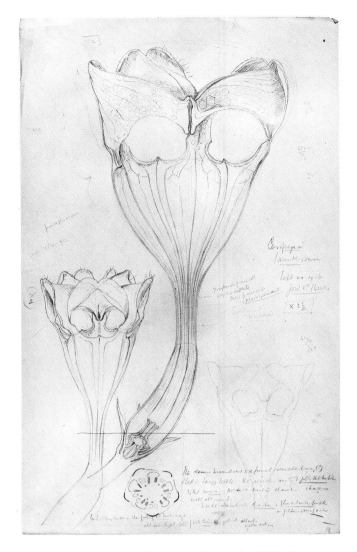

39 *Ceropegia sandersonii* [Decne ex] Hook. f. Working pencil drawing for plate opposite (Church MSS IV (4), Bodleian Library, University of Oxford).

PLATE 57 *Ceropegia sandersonii* [Decne ex] Hook. f. (Asclepiadaceae/Apocynaceae). 26 September 1906. Native to Mozambique and South Africa, this sturdy liane, with a habit of the vanilla orchid, was discovered in 1867 by John Sanderson (1820–1881), a Scot living in Natal: he sent a plant in a Wardian case to Kew the following year.* Like that of *Ceropegia linearis*, the flower of *C. sandersonii* is a pollination trap. The hairs at the apex hang down in still air but in the gentlest breeze start oscillating, creating a strange visual effect. These and the mottling on the corolla are also found in certain *Stapelia* species of the same family and region and are attractive to blow-flies. Insects in *C. sandersonii* climb on to the nectar-cups at the base of the flower and when withdrawing their heads a clip carrying the pollinia is attached; if pollinia are already there, one is caught and comes to rest on the stigma.†

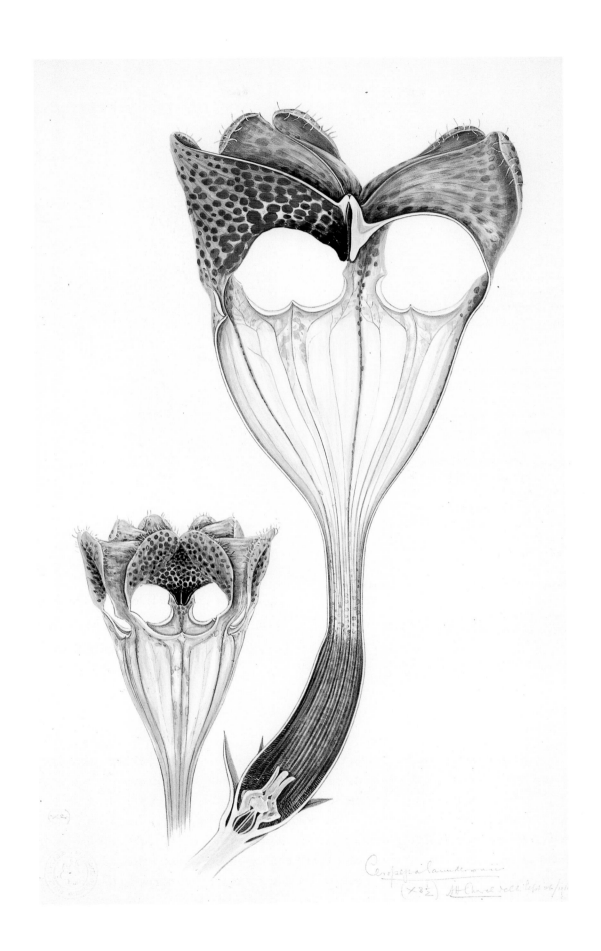

Ceropegia lamderonii
(×3½) St Chevel soll lept 26/oph

'Pretty dickey'

"The culmination of expression of plant-life on this world at the present time is the tree …"

A.H. Church, 'The making of the tree', MSS (1922)

40 Professor E. J.H. [John] Corner (1906–1996) when a young man (private collection).

PLATE 58 Hollyhock *Alcea rosea* L. [*Althaea rosea*] (Malvaceae). October 1904. Allegedly introduced by the Crusaders,* the '*holyhocke*' is mentioned in John Gardener's *Feate of gardening*, a manuscript poem of *c.* 1440, *hoc* being an Anglo-Saxon word for mallow. It may be a hybrid between *A. setosa* (Boiss.) Alef. of Crete and Turkey and *A. pallida* (Willd.) Waldst. & Kit. of central and south-eastern Europe.† *Alcea* comes from the Greek *alkaia*, a kind of mallow; *rosea* = rose-coloured. In Church's time the hollyhock was referred to the genus *Althaea*, after which he named his first daughter Althea, because she was born when it was in flower (see p. 32).

A pupil recalled that, "at the appropriate moment in [Church's] lectures", Tansley became the butt of Church's jokes:

"'Tansley & Miss [Edith] Chick – pause – looked down the same microscope – pause – Miss Chick is now Mrs. Tansley.' This belief in the efficacy in promoting romance led him (at least he told me so) to put two eligible but not very obviously romantic (but very earnest botanically) research students in adjacent rooms with, as he confided to me with a chuckle, the expected result – Miss Pilkington became Mrs Snow [see p. 100]".[1]

Indeed, Church seems to have been something of a matchmaker, as there were several successful marriages as results of his 'Principle of Propinquity'.[2] Church's remark (on such a success on his part) was "All you have to do is to put a couple in the same laboratory and 'propinquity' does the rest!"[3]

"… my own photo of him (taken surreptitiously during a lecture) holding up a double coco-nut [*Lodoicea maldivica*] that looks like the pelvic part of a woman, and leering at the male members of his appreciative audience … I have tender memories of his clipped, condensed rhetoric which required intense concentration during lectures. His humour was dry and often caustic, frequently bawdy – for instance 'Christians wash their bodies, Moslems wash their clothes' – … He spoke of 'depauperate relics of enfeebled land flora' when debunking the evolutionary theories deriving higher plants from mosses and liverworts instead of from his large ± hypothetical tree-like seaweeds. … He could sharpen a razor better than many a barber and cut hand-sections like a microtome."[4]

He preferred free-hand sections:

"'Chips'. He said of them, 'chips'; and showed me his slide of two consecutive free-hand sections through the apical cell of the *Pteridium*-rhizome. He advocated pushing rather than pulling the razor, and would sit with hone beside him to maintain the 'raw edge'; he disliked the strop."[5]

Church published nothing more after 1926 and his lectures became increasingly garrulous: perhaps exhausted, he seems to have lost steam under the new regime. He had had no research students in the modern sense of that term, though Gepp was clearly a convert and disciple. Harry Champion had been a devoted pupil before that, but it was to be a Cambridge man who was to take 'Churchian robustness' forward. John Corner (1906–1996), later Professor E.J.H. Corner CBE, had been introduced to *Thalassiophyta* when a boy at Rugby School and bought his own copy in 1921, when he was 15 (it was later bequeathed to the present author).[6] He wrote later, "Church's sentences were not easy; topics, left now to separate disciplines, are woven into one theme, and the reader must be alert and comprehensive as the author. Thus I ploughed and re-ploughed until I knew much by heart. That copy has accompanied me over the world and, re-reading, I have never failed to gain new insight."[7]

Working as a research student in Cambridge on a "dreary subject on parasitism of mildews given by F.T. Brooks", Corner delivered a paper to the Botany Club, 'Cambridge thoughts on Oxford botany'; Brooks walked out as Corner was concluding and would not speak to him for several weeks. Although Professor Seward was sympathetic to Church, Brooks was against not only Church but Seward as well. Corner

"used to visit those crammed, dusty, and untidy rooms upstairs in the British Museum (Natural History) [The Natural History Museum] which were the Cryptogamic Herbarium, and to discuss Churchian theory with John Ramsbottom …, with Antony Gepp

41 Arthur Harry Church's study at 246 Iffley Road, Oxford (Grattan family).

in his frayed and fragile clothing, and with the big-eyed, gracious Annie Lorrain Smith, wondering the while how any sense of the living world could survive in that overburdened *hortus siccus*: they listened as if 'a young man will be wiser by and by'."[8]

In 1927 Corner was introduced to Church and Church invited him to the Botanic Garden in April 1928 and again in June.[9] He encouraged him in his mycological studies, and among other things Corner brought him material of a huge fungus, *Clavaria pistillaris*, a foot high, which he had found in the Buckinghamshire woods and which astonished Church, who wrote, "I had seen nothing like it before".[10] Corner entered the colonial service

PLATE 59 St Dabeoc's heath *Daboecia cantabrica* (Huds.) K. Koch [*D. polifolia*] (Ericaceae). 3 October 1908. This is a bee-pollinated evergreen heath found from the Azores north to Spain and Ireland.* It was named after Saint Dabeoc (*sic*), also known as Beanus or Mobeoc, a fifth- or sixth-century Cambro-Briton, who left Wales to found a Benedictine monastery on an island in Lough Derg, Donegal, Ireland;† *cantabrica* refers to Cantabria, in north-west Spain.

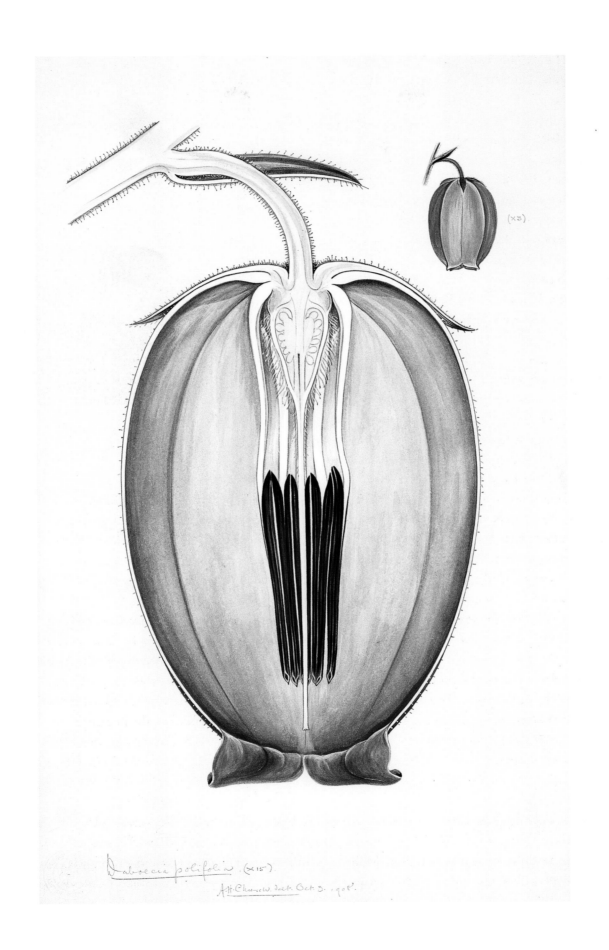

Daboecia polifolia. (×15)

A.H.Church. del. Oct 3. 1908.

(×3).

42 The drawing room at 246 Iffley Road, Oxford (Grattan family).

of seeds,[13] suggesting that the orchid is frequently self-pollinated. Considering it "an interesting study of the complete deterioration of a fine orchid type of the simpler *Dendrobium* form", Church began to work up his initial pencil sketches but got no further.

During Corner's leave from Singapore in 1933–34 he called on Church:

"He was seated stiffly in the upright armchair of the front room, his daughter Grace ever and most kindly attendant. Expression had gone but his eyes twinkled and, on my enquiry of his health, he made the puckish reply, 'pretty dickey'. Those little words near the end of a life of thought conveyed so much."[14]

Indeed, Grace, who attended St Anne's College, Oxford, as a 'home student', studying classics,[15] lived with Church for twenty years after her mother died. Through a mutual friend she met John ('Jack') Grattan, who worked on the London stock exchange, and they planned to marry. Jack, who went on to become a successful nurseryman, met Church just once. By then Church was very ill and frail, for he had had a series of strokes and became paralysed down one side: his speech was gravely affected. His housekeeper, Miss M.T. Learoyd ('Granny Leary'), took over the nursing when Grace and John married in Oxford in 1936 and, after Church's death, went to live with them at Garden Cottage, Sonning Common, Oxfordshire, until she died about 1950.

Church was too ill to attend his daughter's wedding and there was no reception. He died of a further stroke on 24 April 1937, at 246 Iffley Road, in Granny Leary's presence,[16] and was buried at Rose Hill Cemetery in Oxford, in the same grave as his wife and his daughter Rosemary. The only mourners were Grace, Sir Henry Platt (Church's brother-in-law), Elizabeth Coverdale (his sister-in-law and executrix) and her husband, Captain H.S. Blunt (one of his old pupils), and a Miss Crane.[17] His estate was valued at £6462 5s. 9d.[18]

The most important parts of the unpublished manuscript and illustrations for *Types of floral mechanism* were taken for The Natural History Museum, but in 1938–39 Grace entrusted Corner with many other papers, and she

to work as a mycologist at the Botanic Gardens in Singapore. Before he left, Church exhorted him, "Note everything! Draw everything! Photograph everything!" Shortly afterwards, in 1930, Church took early retirement. Arthur ['Roy'] Clapham was appointed departmental demonstrator and, in 1931, university demonstrator, in his place.[11]

Little is recorded of the rest of Church's life, though in June 1931 he made notes and drawings of "a remarkable display [of the white helleborine *Cephalanthera damasonium*] at the beginning of the Icknield Way"[12] on Britwell Hill in the Chilterns to the east of Oxford and returned to see fruiting specimens there in November. The flowers open for only a short time but never open widely, yet almost every flower produces a full capsule

43 Grace Coryla Church in the garden at 246 Iffley Road, Oxford (Grattan family).

presented some watercolours and several books to the library at Sheffield University, where Church's pupil Bentley was professor of botany. Other manuscripts Grace kept under her bed for Corner's later visits, but the outbreak of the Second World War meant that he could not return from Singapore. In 1977 all the papers were reunited, those in Singapore having survived the wartime sacking of Corner's house there by Australian troops, and their subsequent safe-keeping by the Japanese director, who applied his own seal to them; they are all now in the Bodleian Library in Oxford.

Grace Grattan, who had some talent as an artist, later contracted tuberculosis and lost a kidney, but she survived the disease and died, aged 82, in 1989. In 1993 the Grattans' house at Kidmore End, Oxfordshire, was ransacked in a burglary. Fortunately Church's Scrapbook

and microscope were ignored and survive. Grace had two daughters, each of those two more, so that her granddaughter Amanda Anicić (née Watson), now living in Australia, who brought 'Church's Scrapbook to the author's attention, is one of the just six living descendants of Arthur Harry Church.

But Church's heritage is great for, despite having so few blood offspring, there were so many pupils who listened to him at Oxford, particularly those going out to India and the rest of the tropical empire as forest officers. His ideas seeped through to many, but it was to be the research group, set up by Corner in Cambridge on his return to Europe, and his undergraduate teaching there that kept Church's ideas alive in the academic sphere. In 1964, Corner published *The life of plants* — Church would have enjoyed the irony, for Keeble had written a slight treatise, *A life of plants* (1926), long before — which wove Church's ideas and Corner's own elaborations of them into a persuasive narrative, illustrated, in the Church tradition, with the author's own drawings and photographs. It was a bestseller and was translated into many languages, including Japanese.

Corner's own 'durian theory', a controversial thesis on the origin of modern angiosperms from massively constructed precursors, was the intellectual offspring of Church's theorizing. In France, Francis and Nicolas Hallé translated Corner's theory into French, and Francis, with the Dutchman R.A.A. Oldeman, carried the 'tree-architecture' work forward in their *Essai* of 1970. Of Corner's own research students at Cambridge, Timothy Whitmore (born 1935) introduced Flora readers to the theory in the account of the durian family, Bombacaceae, in his *Tree flora of Malaya* (1972), Peter Ashton (born 1934), later a Harvard professor, wrote on ecology and the durian theory,[19] while David Frodin (born 1940), later of Kew, Chiang Kiaw Lan (born 1927) and Ruth Kiew (née Evans; born 1946), both now in Singapore, remain staunch Cornerians. David Mabberley (born 1948) set up a research group when he returned to Oxford in 1973, and, whilst curator of the herbaria in the Department of Sciences there, had the Morphology Laboratory renamed The Church Laboratory. Of his doctoral students, Rowan Jenkins (born 1966), Roger Higton (born

44 Arthur Harry Church (courtesy Amanda Aničić).

intensive instruction and paternal guidance of Oxford undergraduates, to whom he gave his best and earned their gratitude. To most botanists, he was known only by name and as the author of books and papers characterized by clear thinking, provocative, dogmatic statement and bold hypotheses often demanding concentrated thought on the part of readers. Well fitted by ability and breadth of knowledge to occupy the highest positions in his profession, his ambition was to advance science, not himself; life in the laboratory and in the seclusion of home sufficed; to the great regret of colleagues he avoided scientific meetings and social occasions.

Forgetting the idiosyncrasies and regrettable aloofness, we think of Church as a self-sacrificing, devoted, kind-hearted teacher, and as one of the ablest and most original botanists of our time."[21]

1948) and, in particular, Lord Alistair Hay (born 1955), carried the torch onwards.[20]

Seward summed up Church's life in his obituary notice in *Nature*:

"Church was not as other men: he went his own way, indifferent, so it seemed, to the opinions of his fellows; exceptionally able, he combined meticulous accuracy with originality and a flair for discussion. His contributions to botanical science bear the impress of a certain quality of distinction and genius. The greater part of his academic life was spent in

From working-class beginnings in Plymouth, Church had scaled the academic heights, but he had no time for Oxford figures such as Vines and Keeble. He had never been a fellow of a college and thus able to enjoy the prestige of being a don. To soften a life coloured thus and dogged by the deaths of so many of his closest family and pupils and by disappointments in publishing his great works, notably *Types of floral mechanism*, he had resorted to a kind of self-preservation. He made himself the indispensable, yet self-mocking, teacher who wrote 'stunts' and 'jokes', using a kind of humour undergraduates would appreciate.

In his obituary of Church, Tansley spoke of a "genius manqué",[22] because Church's withdrawn nature had not

PLATE 60 Perennial rye-grass *Lolium perenne* L. (Gramineae). 7 October 1904. Like all European grasses, perennial rye-grass is wind-pollinated. It is the main constituent, with clover, of short-rotation leys and is used in lawns, because it withstands trampling: ten times more rye-grass than any other grass is sown every year in the United Kingdom.* It was one of the first grasses deliberately planted to improve pasture and was discussed by Robert Plot in his *Natural history of Oxfordshire* (1677), where it is called 'ray or bennet grass'. Rye-grass is thus not named after rye, *Secale cereale* L. from the Mediterranean region, but is a corruption of *ray*, probably derived from *ivraie*, the French name for darnel, *L. temulentum* L., notorious for a fungal infection that causes its grain to be poisonous;† *Lolium* was the classical name for darnel too.

allowed him to contribute as much as he might otherwise have done. But Tansley was a man who had never had to worry about money, or suffered so much personal sadness. Nonetheless, his slight no doubt reflects the fact that he, too, had a soft side: Church's wit had found its mark. And Tansley really knew that, because of Church's superior knowledge of the facts of botany and brilliance as a lecturer, besides his enormous gifts as an artist, he was writing of not only an elder, but also of a better – a greater man, with a finer mind.

NOTES

1 A.C. Hoyle *in litt.*, 2 February 1978.
2 Cf. Morrell (1997), p. 238, n.
3 F.B.Hora *in litt.*, 20 April 1978.
4 A.C. Hoyle *in litt.*, 2 February 1978.
5 Corner (1981), p. 6.
6 Mabberley, 'Corner' (1999).
7 Corner (1981), p. 3.
8 Corner (1981), p. 2.
9 Church to Corner, 3 April 1928 , 30 June 1928, 23 September 1928, 29 September 1928 (private collection).
10 Corner (1981), p. 6.
11 *Biographical Memoirs of Fellows of the Royal Society*, 39, 1994, p. 77.
12 Church MSS, '*Cephalanthera grandiflora*'.

13 Proctor and Yeo (1973), p. 251–52.
14 Corner (1981), p. 7.
15 J.D.G. Grattan, private communication, via Amanda Aničić, January 2000.
16 Death Certificate, 27 April 1937.
17 *Oxford Times*, 30 April 1937.
18 Probate, Oxford, 12 June 1937 (Ledger 1937, vol. A–C, p. 767); the fate of his drawings and MSS is discussed in Mabberley (1981), pp. 249–52; others, besides Church's Scrapbook and photographs in the family's possession, that have come to light since include 'Practical course – AHC [1894, 1895]', 'AAK from AHC 1935' and 'Oxford 1929', both in the Bodleian Library [ex-Department of Plant Sciences], and two envelopes of manuscripts, one containing notes on maize, sunflowers, *etc.*, a second on 'floral mimicry', both in The Natural History Museum. The widow of Church's pupil Captain H.S. Blunt presented the 'Dr A.H. Church collection' of *c.* 90 photographic plates of Oxford views to the Oxford City Library in 1991. A large collection of botanical photographic plates, also from Blunt but as yet not fully catalogued, is held in the Department of Plant Sciences, Oxford. Church did not amass a herbarium and few of his collections survive except as spirit material, *e.g.* fig flowers, used for teaching. Some specimens were gathered for an ecological herbarium, now incorporated in Druce's herbarium (OXF), and there is a specimen there of *Potamogeton pectinatus* from the Hinksey stream near Oxford, 25 September 1902, as well as a Church drawing of *Bromus interruptus* attached to a Druce specimen, which was the basis for a corbel sculpted in the University Museum in 1910.
19 *Gardens' Bulletin, Singapore*, 29, 1977, pp. 19–23.
20 See, for example, Hay and Mabberley (1991) and (1994).
21 *Nature* 22 May 1937, pp. 870–71.
22 Tansley (1939).

PLATE 61 *Narcissus viridiflorus* Schousboe (Amaryllidaceae). 18 November 1906. This narcissus flowers with the autumn rains in Morocco and the Gibraltar area. The leaves unfold later when the flower stalk elongates, doubling in length and continuing to photosynthesize.* The green flowers are scented at night and are probably moth-pollinated. By comparison with *N. pseudonarcissus* (plate 11), the tubular corona around the stamens is very small. In *Narcissus* "The corona … appears to have arisen as a continuation of ridged outgrowths of the rim of the receptacle-tube between the perianth and the androecium, which had the effect of forming a guard, and limiting the entrance to the floral tube. … Species with only a trace of the corona grade directly into the typical *Amaryllis* construction … but much still remains to be done with regard to determining the lines of evolution of the group. This appears to have been in the Western Mediterranean basin … it is thus possible that the group of Narcissus [there] represents the modern descendants of an ancient, sand-inhabiting, moth-pollinated, Amaryllis-section of a sub-tropical North African flora" (A.H. Church, *Types of floral mechanism*, Part I, 1908, pp. 133–34).

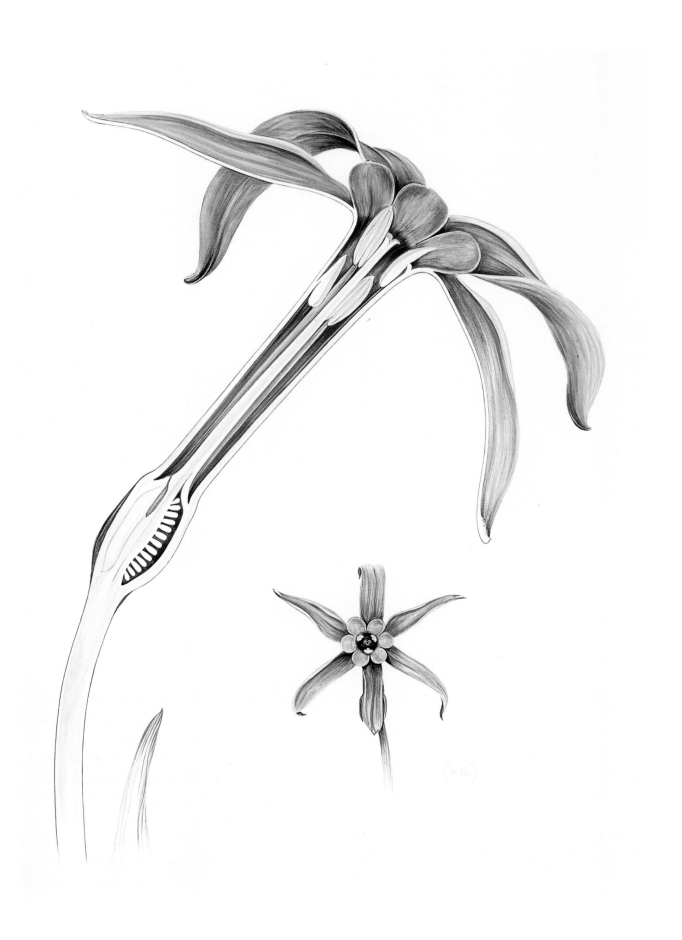

Bibliography

BONEY, A.D., 'A.H. Church's "Thalassiophyta" and the immediate aftermath', *The Psychologist: the Newsletter of the British Psychological Society*, 54, 1999, pp. 2–4

BOWER, F.O., *Sixty years of botany in Britain*, London (Macmillan) 1930

CHURCH, A.H., *Types of floral mechanism*, Part I, Oxford (Clarendon Press) 1908

CLOKIE, H.H., *An account of the herbaria of the Department of Botany in the University of Oxford*, London (Oxford University Press) 1964

CORNER, E.J.H., 'Recollection', in Mabberley (1981), pp. 1–8

GRIGSON, G., *The Englishman's flora*, London (Dent) 1955

GÜNTHER, R.T., *Oxford gardens*, Oxford (Parker) 1912

HAY, A., and MABBERLEY, D. J., '"Transference of function" and the origin of the aroids: their significance in early angiosperm evolution', *Botanische Jahrbücher für Systematik*, 113, 1991, pp. 339–428

HAY, A., and MABBERLEY, D.J., 'On perception of plant morphology: some implications for phylogeny', in Ingram, D.S., and Hudson, A. (eds.), *Shape and form in plants and fungi*, London (Academic Press) 1994, pp. 101–17

HEINE, H., and MABBERLEY, D.J., 'An Oxford waterlily', *Kew Magazine*, 3, 1986, pp. 167–75

HOWARTH, J., 'Science education in late Victorian Oxford: a curious case of failure?', *English Historical Review*, 102, 1987, pp. 334–71

KILLICK, J., PERRY, R., and WOODELL, S., *The flora of Oxfordshire*, Newbury (Pisces) 1998

MABBERLEY, D.J. (ed.), *Revolutionary botany*, Oxford (Clarendon Press) 1981

MABBERLEY, D.J., *Tropical rain forest ecology*, 2nd edn, Glasgow (Blackie) 1992

MABBERLEY, D.J., 'The Oxford Botanical Museum and its fate', *Oxford Plant Systematics*, 3, 1995, pp. 15–16

MABBERLEY, D.J., 'Edred John Henry Corner, C.B.E.', *Biographical Memoirs of Fellows of the Royal Society*, 45, 1999, pp. 77–93

MABBERLEY, D.[J.], *Ferdinand Bauer: the nature of discovery*, London (Merrell Holberton and The Natural History Museum) 1999

MABBERLEY, D.J., *The plant-book: a portable dictionary of the vascular plants*, 2nd edn, 2nd reprint with corrections, Cambridge (Cambridge University Press) 2000

MABBERLEY, D.J., 'Arthur Harry Church', *New dictionary of national biography*, Oxford (Oxford University Press) in press

MORRELL, J., *Science at Oxford 1914–1939*, Oxford (Oxford University Press) 1997

PAVORD, A., *The tulip*, London (Bloomsbury) 1999

PROCTOR, M., and YEO, P., *The pollination of flowers*, London (Collins) 1973

TANSLEY, A.G., 'Arthur Harry Church', *Obituary Notices of Fellows of the Royal Society*, 2, 1939, pp. 433–34

Notes to the Plates and Figures

PLATE 5
*Proctor and Yeo (1973), p. 54.
†Grigson (1955), p. 49; Mabberley (2000), p. 525.

PLATE 7
*Mabberley (2000), p. 364.

PLATE 8
*Mabberley (2000), p. 164.
†C.M. Wilson and D.R. Given, *Threatened plants of New Zealand* (1998), p. 22.

PLATE 9
*Mabberley (2000), p. 434.

PLATE 10
*Mabberley (2000), p. 210.
†Mabberley (2000), p. 296.

PLATE 11
*Church's published drawing was redrawn by Proctor and Yeo (1973), fig. 49.
† H. Gilbert-Carter, *Glossary of the British flora*, 1955, p. 6.

PLATE 13
*A.H. Church, *Oxford Botanical Memoirs* 13, 1922, p. 103.
†Killick, Perry and Woodell (1998), pp. 33, 42, 287.
‡*Oxford Botanical Memoirs* 14, p. 42, n.
§R. Mabey, *Flora britannica*, 1996, p. 406.

PLATE 15
*Proctor and Yeo (1973), p. 240.
†Grigson (1955), p. 424.
‡Killick, Perry and Woodell (1998), p. 298.
§A.M. Pridgen *et al.*, *Lindleyana*, 12, 1997, p. 89.

PLATE 16
*Killick, Perry and Woodell (1998), p. 291.
†Proctor and Yeo (1973), t. 18b.
‡Mabberley (2000), p. 350.

PLATE 18
*Church MSS (*Types of floral mechanism*).
†Heine and Mabberley (1986), pp. 168 *et sqq.*
‡B. Verdcourt, 'Nymphaeaceae', *Flora of tropical east Africa*, (1989), p. 10.

PLATE 19
*Mabberley (2000), p. 411.
†Killick, Perry and Woodell (1998), p. 290.
‡Proctor and Yeo (1973), p. 197.

PLATE 20
*Mabberley (2000), p. 219.

PLATE 21
*Pavord (1999), pp. 58, 271, 387.

PLATE 22
*Mabberley (2000), p. 493.
†Grigson (1955), p. 48.

PLATE 23
*Working drawing reproduced in Mabberley (1981), t. 17.
†B.E. Juniper, R.J. Robins and D.M. Joel, *The carnivorous plants*, 1989, pp. 14–15, 37, 195, 270.
‡Mabberley (2000), p. 640.

PLATE 24
*Mabberley (2000), p. 424.
†A.R. Clapham *et al.*, *Flora of the British Isles*, 3rd edn, 3, 1987, p. 88.
‡*Journal of the Arnold Arboretum*, 68, 1987, p. 192.
§Killick, Perry and Woodell (1998), p. 138.

PLATE 26
*W.T. Stearn and P.H. Davis, *Peonies of Greece*, 1984, pp. 20–21.

PLATE 28
*Mabberley (2000), p. 424.

PLATE 29
*Proctor and Yeo (1973), p. 232.

PLATE 30
*Mabberley (2000), p. 118.

PLATE 31
*Killick, Perry and Woodell (1998), p. 297.

PLATE 33
*D.J. Mabberley and P.J. Placito, *Algarve plants and landscape*, 1993, p. 49.
†A.M. Coats, *Flowers and their histories* (1968), p. 25.

PLATE 34
*Mabberley (2000), p. 745.
†*Oxford English dictionary*, 'faba'.

PLATE 35
*Proctor and Yeo (1973),
pp. 117–18.
†H. Baumann, *The Greek plant world
in myth, art and literature*, trans.
W.T. and E.R. Stearn, 1993, p. 126.

PLATE 36
*Mabberley (2000), pp. 634–35.
†Proctor and Yeo (1973), p. 122.

PLATE 37
*Mabberley (2000), p. 223.
†*Oxford English dictionary*, 'william'.
‡R. Vickery, *A dictionary of plant
lore*, 1995, pp. 363–64.

PLATE 38
*Mabberley (2000), p. 525.

PLATE 39
*Proctor and Yeo (1973), p. 179.
†Killick, Perry and Woodell
(1998), p. 178.
‡A.M. Coats, *Flowers and their
histories*, 1968, p. 86.

PLATE 42
*Proctor and Yeo (1973), p. 215.
†Killick, Perry and Woodell
(1998), p. 186.
‡Mabberley (2000), p. 276.

PLATE 43
*Working drawing reproduced in
Mabberley (1981), t. 19.
†Mabberley (2000), p. 532.

PLATE 44
*Mabberley (2000), p. 356.
†Grigson (1955), p. 291.
‡R. Vickery, *A dictionary of plant
lore*, 1995, pp. 177–78.

PLATE 45
*R. Vickery, *A dictionary of plant
lore*, 1995, p. 35.
†Mabberley (1992) p. 174.

PLATE 47
*Mabberley (2000), p. 290.
†Proctor and Yeo (1973), p. 319.

PLATE 49
*Proctor and Yeo (1973),
pp. 244–46.

PLATE 52
*Mabberley (2000), p. 228.
†Mabberley, *Bauer* (1999), p. 114.

PLATE 53
*Mabberley (2000), p. 166.

PLATE 54
*Mabberley (2000), p. 730.

PLATE 55
*Mabberley (2000), p. 332.

PLATE 56
*Proctor and Yeo (1973),
pp. 302–03.

PLATE 57
*J.D. Hooker, *Botanical Magazine*,
t. 5792 (1869), t. 5792.
†Proctor and Yeo (1973),
pp. 303–04.

PLATE 58
A.M. Coats, *Flowers and their histories*
(1968), p. 12.
†Mabberley (2000), p. 21.

PLATE 59
*Mabberley (2000), p. 210.
†http://www.erols.com/saintpat/
ss/0101.htm (J. Bennett, personal
communication).

PLATE 60
*Killick, Perry and Woodell
(1998), p. 272.
†A. Arber, *The Gramineae* (1934),
p. 145.

PLATE 61
*Mabberley (2000), p. 478.

FIGURE 7
* J. Britten, 'Anne Pratt', *Journal of
Botany*, 32, 1894, pp. 205–07.

FIGURE 16
*Mabberley (2000), pp. 410–11.

FIGURE 18
*Mabberley (2000), p. 747.

FIGURE 21
*Mabberley (2000), p. 288.

FIGURE 23
*Mabberley (2000), p. 331;
working drawing now in the
Bodleian Library, reproduced in
Mabberley (1981), t. 20.

FIGURE 24
*Killick, Perry, and Woodell

(1998), p. 97.

FIGURE 26
*Church, *Oxford Botanical Memoirs*,
12, (1921), pp. 12–3.
†Mabberley (2000), p. 452.

FIGURE 28
*Working drawing reproduced in
Mabberley (1981), t. 26.

FIGURE 30
**Obituary Notices, Fellows of the Royal
Society*, 1, 1932, pp. 12–14.
†Clokie (1964), pp. 50, 158.

FIGURE 37
*Mabberley (1981), p. vii.

Index

CONTENTS

ADVISORY BOARD AND JURY

Each year we appoint an advisory board to assist in nominating and judging images for the EXPOSE awards. All of these people are either leading artists in their own right or are experienced and respected editors and reviewers of digital content and artists.

Syd Mead is one of the most celebrated concept designers of our time. His most well-known works include production designs for 'Blade Runner', 'TRON', 'Aliens' and '2010', the pivotal science fiction movies that got many budding visual effects artists inspired to enter professional careers in this field.

Lorne Lanning is President/Creative Director and Co-Founder of the award-winning video game development company Oddworld Inhabitants. He serves as a member of the Visual Effects Society, the Wired Brain Trust, as well as the Executive Vice Chairman of the Academy of Interactive Arts and Sciences.

Eric Hanson is a visual effects designer specializing in the creation of digital environments and effects for feature films. Hanson has worked on 'The Day After Tomorrow', 'Spider-Man', 'Cast Away', 'Hollow Man', 'Mission to Mars', 'Bicentennial Man', 'Atlantis' and 'The Fifth Element', among others.

Tim McGovern, a Visual Effects Supervisor, began in CGI in 1981 when he started working at Robert Abel & Associates. Tim was a founding member of MetroLight Studios where the visual effects X-ray Skeleton sequence for 'Total Recall' earned him an Academy Award in 1992.

Scott Robertson is a luminary of the LA concept design community. He graduated with honors at Art Center College of Design with a B.S. degree in Transportation Design. Scott founded Design Studio Press, co-authoring 'Concept Design' and writing 'How to Draw Vehicles'.

Christopher Sloan is the Art Director for the National Geographic Magazine. Sloan is also the magazine's specialist in paleontology and paleoanthropology, writing articles for National Geographic including 'Feathers for T. rex' as well as several award-winning children's books.

Dan Curry is VFX Producer/Supervisor for 'Star Trek: Enterprise'. Dan has worked on the 'Star Trek' TV series since 1987, first as visual effects supervisor on 'Star Trek: The Next Generation', and then as Visual Effects Producer on 'Star Trek: The Next Generation', 'Star Trek: Deep Space Nine', and 'Star Trek: Voyager'.

Jeff Mottle is President and Founder of www.CGarchitect.com and is the Creative Director—North America for Smoothe, an award winning design firm based in London, Manchester and Calgary. Jeff has also worked for SMED International, one of the world's largest construction industry leaders.

Stephan Martiniere is an internationally renowned Science Fiction and Fantasy artist. He is also an accomplished concept artist who has worked on movies such as 'I, Robot', 'Star Wars' Episodes 2 & 3, 'Red Planet', and 'The Time Machine'. Stephan is currently the visual design director for Midway Games in Chicago.

Kim Bauman Larsen is a licensed Norwegian architect and the CEO and founding partner of PLACEBO EFFECTS. He has done computer visualization for over a decade and lectured at architecture schools in Scandinavia and the US. His works are published in magazines and shown on network television.

THE EDITORS

Daniel Wade | Managing Editor & Paul Hellard | Assistant Editor of Ballistic Publishing

The EXPOSÉ series of annuals is the flagship of Ballistic Media's goal to advance and grow the digital arts industry worldwide. With the official launch of EXPOSÉ 2 at SIGGRAPH 2004, it took just six months to sell out the initial print-run and organise the printing of the 2nd Edition.

The Call for Entries for EXPOSÉ 3 also started at SIGGRAPH 2004, and in the six-month entry period another record number of entries were received. The styles of entries and their subject matter continued to evolve and this year we created new categories to keep up with this evolution. The new categories were: Surreal; Robotic/Cyborg; Creature in Repose; and Cityscapes. The addition of these categories allowed us to expand to meet the growing numbers of architectural and character entries that cover so many styles. With the growth of entries, we decided to grow EXPOSÉ 3 by an additional sixteen pages to make sure we included as many artists as we could fit. EXPOSÉ 3 is also the first time we have differentiated the pages of the Limited Edition to the softcover and hardcover editions. EXPOSÉ 3 Limited Edition features a sixteen page feature on the Grand Master and Master award winners for each category with extra artwork and artist information.

Beyond the number of entries, another measure of success for Ballistic Media is where the artists who enter their work into EXPOSÉ come from. It was extremely gratifying for the Ballistic team to see entries from more countries than the previous EXPOSÉ, and we are pleased to welcome entrants from Bangladesh, Barbados, Colombia, Costa Rica, Ecuador, Honduras, Jordan, Lebanon, Lithuania, Moldova, Pakistan and Peru. Entrants literally came from the four corners of the globe to EXPOSÉ 3 from a total of 71 countries.

We were extremely fortunate to secure the talents of an Advisory Board renowned for their work in the field of CG. Luminaries such as Syd Mead, Chris Sloan and Lorne Lanning returned after their stint as EXPOSÉ 2 board members and Jeff Mottle, an authority in the architectural visualization area, rejoined us from the EXPOSÉ 1 board.

The number of entries for EXPOSÉ 3 increased by 25% over EXPOSÉ 2. Though this added a little more difficulty to the judging process, it was the jump in quality of entries that made every category a painstaking task to narrow down. On average one in 25 entries were successful in EXPOSÉ 3 (down from one in four for EXPOSÉ 1 and one in fifteen for EXPOSÉ 2). The preselection process alone took almost one week to complete narrowing down the almost-5,000 entries into manageable numbers of 50-70 entries per category for the judging to begin.

The Advisory Board used our online judging system to narrow down their ten preferred entries for each category which we then tallied to determine the award winners for those categories. The top images were awarded Master Awards and depending on merits 1-4 images received Excellence Awards in each category. In all, the whole judging process took around two weeks to complete narrowing down the initial 5,000-odd entries down to 248 images from 182 artists for printing in EXPOSÉ 3. The artists came from 37 different countries. Roughly half of the entries were 3D and half 2D (digital paintings)—a big jump for 2D from EXPOSÉ 2.

Easily the hardest part of the whole EXPOSÉ process was agonizing over all the fantastic images entered that we just did not have room to print. The quality of the entries was astounding this year, and only one in twenty-five images made it into the book, compared to one in fifteen for EXPOSÉ 2. We continue to explore ways to promote all of the talented artists who were not featured in EXPOSÉ.

Finally, we have managed to keep the entry process completely free and we are offering all the featured artists free hardcover copies of the book. So please, rave about the book, show it to all your friends and then go on-line and see all the work and join in yourself and tell us what you think!

FANTASY

The Fantasy category honors the highest achievement in the mythic fantasy style. Here, the artist's talent in evoking an emotional response or attachment with the image is paramount. This category focuses on the mythic or fairytale aspects of the work. Excellence in all technical aspects is a must so as to create the evocation of atmosphere required. As with EXPOSÉ 2, a significant percentage of the EXPOSÉ 3 entries met the fantasy criteria with most opting for the traditional faeries and dragons.

Of all the categories for EXPOSÉ 3, Fantasy was the one that could have easily become its own book. Of the five hundred images in the category, the judges narrowed the field down to seventeen. Not surprisingly, over half of those selected were award winners. All of the selected entries showed off the artist's great technical skills, while also meeting the main criteria of evoking an emotional response. The successful entries all combined a storytelling theme hinting at a depth of character and story beyond the

captured moment. The Master award winner for the Fantasy 2D category was Matt Gaser with 'Gluba Vander Hon the Giant'. Deak Ferrand, Martin Lisec and Kornél Ravadits picked up Excellence awards for the 2D category. The Master award winner for the Fantasy 3D category was Steven Stahlberg with 'The King's Fairy Catcher'. Laurent Pierlot, Alexander Hedstrom, Olivier Ponsonnet and Sang Hyun Bang picked up the Excellence awards in the 3D category.

ARCHITECTURAL

An ever growing number of architectural entries made it necessary to create a new sister category of Cityscapes for EXPOSÉ 3. This separation allowed us to show a wider selection of exterior pieces across the two categories. The Architectural category honors the best architectural visualization, independent of style or setting. The defining criterion here is the artist's ability to create an image that is not just believable but is inspirational, and in particular evokes a desire to visit the

location/building/space. The Architectural category was dominated by interior visualizations for EXPOSÉ 3 encompassing restaurants, galleries, corporate settings, performance spaces, recreation areas and even a yacht interior. Of all the successful entries in this category the common link between each scene was well-executed lighting set-ups. With each new EXPOSÉ, it's the Architectural category that most clearly shows the progress in lighting tools and techniques that help to produce

more realistic visualizations. Another important technical skill is the correct choice of camera optics which simulates the results that a traditional photographer would achieve. The Master Award for the Architectural 3D category was Jorgen Bork for 'Almost White Room' visualizing a home entertainment space. All of the architectural visualizations were created in 3D which meant that there was no 2D sub-category and subsequently no Master or Excellence award winners for 2D.

CHARACTER IN REPOSE

Restrictions, Photoshop, Painter
Jiansong Chen, CHINA

Similar to the Architectural category, the character design categories were overflowing with entries for EXPOSÉ 3. The solution was to create two new categories of Creature in Repose and Robotic/Cyborg to accommodate the many great character studies. The criteria for Character in Repose was for artists to create organic characters encompassing technical skill, believability, composition and, most of all, emotion. The overall challenge was to test the artist's ability to bring their characters to life.

The level of artistry in the Character in Repose category was phenomenal with serious competition for the Master awards in both the 2D and 3D categories. The eventual winner for Character in Repose 2D Master was 'Existence' by Jose Manuel Fernandez Oli producing a wonderfully expressive character in an interesting setting. Other notable entries in the 2D category included 'Chinese Persons of Ancient Times' by Weng Ziyang, 'Your Eyes Would Explode (If You Had Seen What I Have Seen)' by Jack Youngblood

and 'Trading In Danger' by Dave Seeley. The 3D category was dominated by Eun-Hee Choi with two pieces: 'Oriental Heroine' and 'Oriental Hero'. Both of these character studies were stunning, and 'Oriental Heroine' was an early frontrunner and an eventual choice for the EXPOSÉ 3 cover. Pascal Blanché, the Grand Master award winner, was also well represented in this category. Overall, the Character in Repose category was an excellent example of the jump in the quality of entries for EXPOSÉ 3.

CHARACTER IN ACTION

On the way II, Photoshop
Xiao Yi, CHINA

The Character in Action category honors the highest achievement in capturing a character in a state of movement. This category celebrates the artist that best captures the sheer power, energy and elegance of a character in motion. Although many digital artists aspire to create animations that come to life, it is a rare talent to capture expressive motion frozen in a moment in time. The majority of entries for Character in Action were in the 2D category with only 25% in 3D.

A possible reason for the imbalance is that 3D characters, require a great deal of technical skill to produce a believable result. Add to this the complication of movement and the bar is set very high to achieve a great result. Finally, it takes courage to blur painstakingly-created details in pursuit of an expressive moment in time. The Master award for the Character in Action 2D category was won by the prolific and overly-talented Stephan Martiniere (who as an Advisory

Board member for EXPOSÉ 3 excused himself from the judging of this category for 'Monster'. Notable entries in the category included 'Turtle' by Dave Seeley, 'Undead Encounter' by Martin Bergstrom and 'Springheeled Jack 1' by Aaron McBride. The Master Award for Character in Action category was won for 'Octopus' by Platinum. Other notable entries included 'Kinnaree' by Udom Ruangpaisitporn, '3K-Athlete' by Carlos Bernardo Delgado Virgen and 'Calito' by Renaud de Bellefon

CREATURE IN REPOSE

Oddworld Stranger's Wrath: Hero Pose
Photoshop, Maya, Oddworld Inhabitants, USA

A new category for EXPOSÉ 3, Creature in Repose recognizes the greatest talent in breathing life and personality into a creature. This is independent of style or of the organic nature of the character. The defining criterion is the artist's ability to bring the creature to life. This encompasses technical skill, believability, composition and, perhaps most of all, emotion. The new category offered the opportunity to feature characters which would previously have been categorized in the Character in

Repose or Fantasy categories. The entries for the inaugural Creature in Repose category included game characters, movie-inspired categories and personal creations. Advisory Board member Lorne Lanning abstained from voting in this category, though this did not affect the high number of votes for several stills from Oddworld Inhabitant's 'Oddworld Stranger's Wrath'. The Master award for Creature in Repose 2D went to 'Riis, Lost in his Thoughts' by Pierre Droal. The rest of the 2D award winners spanned

the gamut of interpretations of creatures with alien-type beings, a regular pet cat and a hybrid elephant creature which defies description. The Master award for Creature in Repose 3D went to the highly talented Fred Bastide for 'My Uncle Cthulhu' who also won an Excellence award in EXPOSÉ 2 in the Character in Repose category. Other notable entries in the 3D category were 'Oddworld Stranger's Wrath: Hero Pose' by Oddworld Inhabitants, 'Bumble-bee' by Eugene Rabok and 'Mole Warrior' by Pete Sussi.

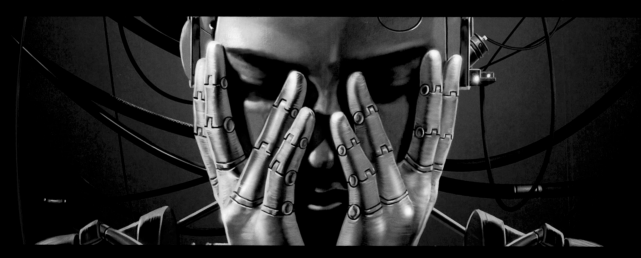

ROBOTIC/CYBORG

Painful Upgrade, Painter
Mark Evans, USA

A new category for EXPOSÉ 3, Robotic/ Cyborg was another category that lent itself to the abundance of character studies with a biomechanical theme. The Robotic/Cyborg category recognizes the highest achievement in bringing a robotic or cyborg character into existence. The defining criterion is the artist's ability to create a believable being whether totally mechanical, or a composite of organic being and machine. This encompasses technical skill, believability, composition and most

of all, emotion. This new category couldn't help but benefit from the Machineflesh CG Challenge run on CGTalk/CGNetworks with a handful of entries finding their way into EXPOSÉ 3. Many of the entries in this category were very successful in eliciting an emotional response. This is no small achievement considering that the characters with personality are metal. The Master award for the Robotic/Cyborg 2D category went to the atmospheric and confronting 'Synergy' by Eddie Smith. Notable entries in the 2D

category included the slightly disturbing 'Vision' by Jason Felix, and 'Click Drones' by Sparth. The Master Award winner for the Robotic/Cyborg 3D category went to the talented Meats Meier for 'The Last of the Leaves'. Meats was also a Master award winner for EXPOSÉ 1 for Visual Effects and an Excellence winner for Character in Repose. Notable 3D entries in Robotic/ Cyborg included 'Xspace' by Ngo Hock Lim, 'Robot Carriste' by Bouchet Christophe and 'CyberSamurai' by Andrea Bertaccini.

ABSTRACT & DESIGN

Feelings, Fractal Explorer
Titia van Beugen, NETHERLANDS

The Abstract & Design category recognizes the most outstanding image that is predominantly abstract. Here, the artist's design and artistic expression are paramount in creating an image that defies categorization and excels in its pure design and visual appeal. Many of the difficult to categorize entries found a home in the Abstract & Design category. The number of entries in this category doubled from EXPOSÉ 2 making the choice of styles to feature all the more challenging. The category was well represented by fractal-type illustrations along with more current exploded abstract designs and familiar traditional designs. The Master award winning entry for this category 'The Household' by Cherie Treweek offered a remarkable design with intricate elements that can take several viewings. The Excellence award winners covered the gamut of styles with notable entries including 'Avian Paranoia' by Dan Blomberg, 'Sequential Escalation' by Brandon Williams and 'Crystal Light' by Agnes Dodart. The Master Award for Abstract & Design 3D went to Tim Borgmann for 'Shape.92#2'. In addition to cleaning up in this category with two more Excellence awards, Tim was also the Master award winner in this category for EXPOSÉ 2. Other notable entries in this category included 'Au Petit Matin' by Renaud Louis, Tomasz Opasinski for his two Graffiti pieces and Ryan Etter for his 'Armor' and 'Time' designs.

HUMOROUS

The (last) Flight Of A Mouse
Maya, mental ray, Photoshop, Igor Kudryavtsev, RUSSIA

The Humorous category recognizes the most amusing image, whether 2D or 3D, cartoon, humorous, satirical or just plain ridiculous. This category is all about making the viewer smile and even laugh out loud. The Humorous category is a difficult category to fill thanks to the subjective nature of the humorous reaction. What one person finds hysterically funny might only elicit a smirk from someone else. Away from the fringes, a number of entries made the category easier to judge. Many of the entries opted for the "bread and butter" approach to humor with cute characters with exaggerated features. However, even these entries plumbed a deeper level of humor through the character's situation or their surroundings. As a departure from the entries in EXPOSÉ 2, few successful entries opted for a satirical approach. The judging for the 2D category was surprisingly close with the Master award going to Bobby Chiu for his wonderfully executed 'Three Samurai on Horseback' The remaining plaudits for the Humorous 2D category went to Elena Sedova for two entries titled 'Just Married' and 'Crazy Cat'. 'Life is a leaf' by Xiao Yi was also a notable entry with great character expressions. The Master award winner for Humorous 3D was Nenad Jalsovec for 'Ceremonial Cat II (Cat no. 4)'. Notable entries for Humorous 3D category included 'Valentine's Day Piglet', 'The (last) Flight Of A Mouse' by Igor Kudryavtsev and 'Automatic Milking Machine' by Ila Soleimani.

SURREAL

A new category for EXPOSÉ 3, Surreal recognizes the highest achievement in bringing a surreal character or scene into being. The defining criterion is the artist's ability to create a dreamlike or nightmarish scene which invokes an emotional response ranging from wonder to disturbance. This encompasses technical skill, composition and, perhaps more than any other category, emotion. Not surprisingly, there were several Dali-esque entries in this category with one particular entry 'Out-Dali-ing' Dali according to one of the Advisory Board members for its disturbing content. There were also other styles of surreal paintings represented with several montage pieces inspired by the work of Hieronymous Bosch and Rene Magritte. The inaugural Surreal category was dominated in the judging by Teodoru Badiu with 'The Painted Horse' winning him the Master award for the Surreal 2D category. Teodoru also received an Excellence award in the category along with Egil Paulsen for 'Furioso deluge' an Francesco D'Isa for 'Unfinished but ended Teodoru Badiu also won the Master awar for the Surreal 3D category along wit an unprecedented two Excellence awar rounding out a near-sweep of the category 'Ripeness' was a great combination c the surreal and the humorous, makin it a worthy Master award winner. Als recognised in the Surreal 3D category wa the hugely talented Christos Maggana with his beautifully executed 'Thallasa'.

TRANSPORT

The Transport category awards the best device for moving about in. Whether exotic vehicle, classical Venetian gondola or animal to be ridden, this category seeks out the best images of transportation. The defining quality sought after here is the artist's ability to capture and evoke the desire to travel to a place, or by a mode of transport or to travel in a particular way. The modes of transport represented in the category varied from space travel futuristic vehicles, hot air balloon and animal transport. The standard of entry for the Transport category was exceptional and in an eerily similar situation to the Environment 2D category in EXPOSÉ 2, Stephan Martiniere managed to win multiple awards (even while abstaining from the voting). Though the voting across the whole EXPOSÉ book was uniformly close, the Transport category saw the Master award winners take out their categories with huge margins. Nick Pugh won the Master award for the Transport 2D category with 'Liquid Car'. Stephan Martiniere cleaned up the rest of the Excellence awards in the 2D category with his paintings '0' 'Nautilus' and 'Skinner'. The clear Maste award winner for Transport 3D wa Michael Sormann for 'T.P.Barracuda'. The Excellence award winners in the category went to Daniel Trbovic for 'Marser', Razvar Maftei for 'Ducati on Street', Fred Bastide for 'Helix Rugens 1' (a finalist in the Granc Space Opera CG Challenge) and Riza Endartama for 'Palm Tungsten LM'

Glade, Photoshop, Painte
Chris Beatrice, USA

ENVIRONMENT

The Environment category recognizes the best set or location. This could be indoors, outdoors, underwater, in space—wherever. Here, the artist's ability to evoke a sense of wonder and a wish to see more is paramount. This category demands a combination of artistic interpretation, detail and lighting to create a believable and enticing (or evocative) environment. The successful entries for this category varied greatly in scale and subject material, from vast panoramas to building interiors and

geological features. Half of the successful entries made great use of atmospherics such as mist and dust to add an extra dimension to the scene. The 2D category was overloaded with outstanding entries. The Master award for Environment 2D went to Gary Tonge for 'The Room' after winning an Excellence for the same category in EXPOSÉ 2. The Excellence award winners in the Environment 2D category included: 'Old Unused Passage' by Ales Horak, 'In the Jungle' by Emrah Elmasli and 'Dubrovnik

Matte Painting' by Patrick Jensen. The Environment 3D category was even more packed with quality images with four Excellence awards. The Master award for Environment 3D went to Frederic St-Arnaud for 'Waterfall Castle'. The Excellence award winners for the category included 'Mantra' by Thomas Juul Krahn, 'Notre Dame Sunday' by Luciano Neves (the Master award winner for the category in EXPOSÉ 2), 'La Hacienda' by Daniel Schmid Leal and 'Birdhouse' by Clement Choblet.

City Plateaus, Photoshop
Dylan Cole, USA

CITYSCAPES

A new category for EXPOSÉ 3, Cityscapes recognizes the greatest talent in realizing a cityscape independent of time or space. The defining criterion is the artist's ability to create a city or civilization which entices the viewer to virtually visit a city of the past, present or future. This encompasses technical skill, believability, composition and, perhaps most of all, mood. The new category allowed us to segment the Architectural category to feature more interior visualizations. The

Cityscapes category attracted a large number of matte painting style scenes. At the pinnacle of these matte paintings in the 2D category was Master award winner Dylan Cole with 'City Plateaus'. Dylan is a renowned matte painting artist whose recent work has included 'Lord of the Rings: Return of the King', 'The Chronicles of Riddick', 'I, Robot', 'Van Helsing', 'Sky Captain and the World of Tomorrow', and 'The Aviator'. Other notable entries in the 2D category included 'Avanty World'

by Sparth, concept art from the movie 'I, Robot' by Stephan Martiniere and his 'A Shadow in Summer'. The Master award for the Cityscapes 3D category went to Rudolf Herczog for 'Traffic'. The Excellence award winners for the 3D category included 'Warfare and Harmony' by La Hodong (which was also a finalist in the Grand Space Opera CG Challenge), 'Fantasy Life' by Jir Adamec and 'Memories of my hometown' by Wang Banyun

Mark Snoswell & Leonard Teo | Founders of Ballistic Media, Ballistic Publishing,
CGSociety, CGTalk, CGNetworks, CGWorkshops, and CGProshop

Ballistic Media is just two years old. We established Ballistic Publishing to fund our global community of digital artists—CGTalk.com and CGNetworks.com. Between the books, conferences and advertising this has been hugely successful. The community has grown exponentially, and we have been able to add many new features and services while keeping everything free. At the same time we have done our best to lead the community, to implement guidelines, forum leadership and community-building activities like the Challenges. Now the CGNetworks community is the highest profile, strongest, largest and most dynamic group of digital arts professionals in the world.

As this book goes to press we are proud to announce the next stage in our growth: the CGSociety. This brings together everything we have been doing already—the community, the conferences, the awards, the training. The CGSociety will deliver member benefits in four main areas: events; training; publications; and artist promotions. There is way too much to cover here in detail and we invite everyone to visit us online, learn more, and join in!

CGSociety Manifesto

The CGSociety is for Creative Digital Artists. This is anyone who uses computers to tell a visual story. No matter what the format or scope, from a still image to a complete film or game, telling a visual story is the thread that ties this community together. The CGSociety seeks to enhance the global state of creative digital arts. It celebrates, aggregates, supports, trains and promotes creative digital artists in their local and global communities. It's also way cool!

The CGSociety is the most respected and accessible global organization for creative digital artists. It is unbiased in its enthusiastic support of all genres, styles, tools and outlooks. It supports professional chapters in: Film; Games; Concept Design; and Visualization. It celebrates everyone from enthusiastic beginners to industry leaders in every aspect of our community: pure artists; designers; animators; directors; programmers; producers; and hardware developers.

The CGSociety offers value in a number of areas: publications; events; training; and artists promotions. Among these will be: special discounts and access to books, the CGN magazine and products on CGProshop; privileged access to CGNetworks, CGTalk and CGSociety web sites and services; the CGConference and film festivals; the CGAwards; CGPortfolio; member and industry promotions.

Above all the CGSociety will be the coolest and best way for creative digital artists to further their individual and collective goals.

Creative digital artists—we salute you all

Creative digital artists strive to re-create the world around us and to extend it into future, alternate and fantasy realms. This includes: product design; character design; animation; architectural visualization; game design; matte painting; visual effects; and film design. More than just creating impressive work, the creative digital artist is characterized by the desire to reach out and touch the viewer—evoking a desire, a feeling, an empathy or a laugh.

No matter what the genre (fantasy, realistic, surreal, concept, manga), style, or number of dimensions (2D, 3D, 4D), creative digital artists have been empowered by a rich set of digital tools. Fueled by artistic desire and the never-ending onslaught of new hardware and software, the creative digital artist has a foot in two worlds—they must be super artist and super nerd at the same time. The CGSociety brings together the creative digital artists and the whole community that supports, supplies and enjoys their endeavors.

The tools and technology available now enable the digital artists to go way beyond the images and animations created by traditional hand methods. Digital artists can mimic reality or create fantasy with greater intensity and believability than ever before. Add interaction and the viewer now becomes a player or participant in the digital artist's world.

Elven Warrior
Photoshop, Painter
Cho Kyoung-Min, KOREA

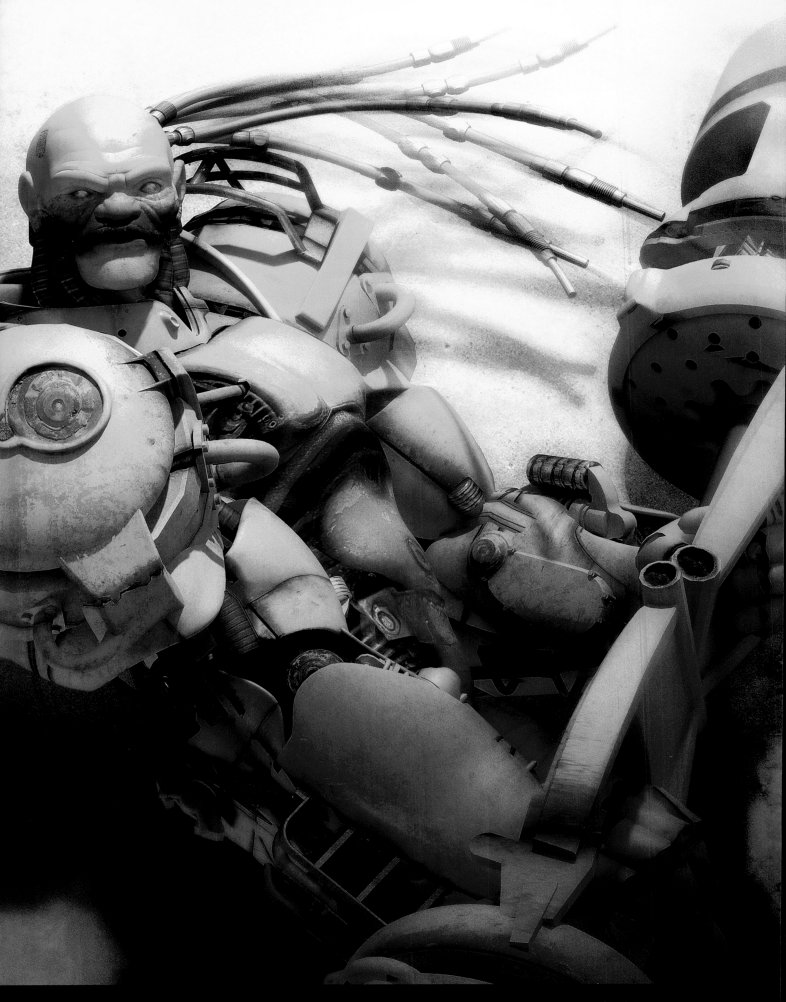

Grand Master
Pascal Blanché

Gladiator
3ds max, Photoshop, VRay
Pascal Blanché, Ubisoft, CANADA

GRAND MASTER

The EXPOSÉ 3 Grand Master Award winner Pascal Blanché shares his insight into the realm of 3D art today. Starting out as an art student in southern France, Blanché is now a prominent art director in one of the world's biggest gaming conglomerates, Ubisoft.

As far back as he can remember, Pascal Blanché has always had a pen in his hand. He was the guy at school drawing monsters on the corner of tables.

Beginnings
"I remember standing in my father's photographic darkroom, watching all those magic white papers turn into portraits, landscapes, and insects close-ups. I was five years old, maybe less but I think that I'm more receptive to framing and composition because of this early experience. Later, I spent all my free time in libraries, comic shops or movie theatres, watching 'The Empire Strikes Back' or 'Raiders of the Lost Ark' for the tenth time. I was also watching Ray Harryhausen's movies late at night and making puppets out of socks and ping-pong balls."

First Steps
During his last years of art school, Blanché started to send CG pictures to the galleries of video game magazines. From this, he landed a job at Tilt magazine, the biggest French video game magazine at the time. "Then came a day when I jumped at the opportunity of my life. The official illustrator was out for holidays, the magazine was doing its first publication in full digital process and they needed a full-page illustration for their game test. I told the boss I could work Photoshop on a Mac. Of course, it was my first illustration with Photoshop, and the one button mouse was a nightmare to use, but I managed to get more illustration work after that, and my own column about CG drawing."

Movies
"In 2000, I moved to Canada and worked for a year as an animator, then lead animator on the first French/Canadian full CG movie

'Kaena: the Prophecy', distributed by Sony. It was the first time a production of this scale used only standard out-of-the-box software and hardware. It was also the first time I had such a specialized animation assignment. The quality and level of complexity of this assignment was very high, and it really was a tough job. I remember animating a scene with ten human-like characters moving around and interacting each other at the same time—a real nightmare! Unfortunately, the production of the sequel was stopped. This was a pity because with the experience we'd gained, the second movie would have been interesting to do."

Fun and games
Tilt magazine closed its doors, and Blanché found his first assignment in the video game industry with a little company called Virtual Xperience, where he worked with five other guys on a video game for three years. "I started creating characters in clay, then used a digital camera to take a picture of each pose and reproduce the whole animation with an Amiga 2000. The result wasn't bad considering the tools we had, but the hard drive melted and destroyed our work. We started over the whole visual in 3D with 3dstudio 4, the DOS version of what we now know as 3ds max. I learned every aspect of the software—from modeling and texturing, to lighting and animation. After two years of hard work, the game, 'Atripolis 2097' was almost done, with almost 50 minutes of cinematics, a whole city entirely modeled and its little citizens running everywhere. Then the boss came in and pulled the plug on the entire project. After that I worked two years at Xilam Studios on the adaptation of a French kid's cartoon called 'Home to rent'. I was in charge of the modeling of the characters and lead cinematics.

Thomas Szabo, the director and scriptwriter of the project was also one of the scenarists of the series. He taught me a lot about framing and storyboarding; how to place a camera; how to tell a story in a few shots. He would come in on Monday morning with a few strips and act out the entire cinematic in front of me. With no time for full modeling, half the time I was animating and modeling what I had in the frame, and the other half mixing up little recipes on After Effects to save time. Within three weeks, and after a lot of coffee, my first game was released."

Video game industry
"I've been working in the video game field for eleven years now, and I still smile in the morning when I go to work. Working in video games is more about working with people. I still learn from my co-workers and each production has its own energy. I've worked in small companies with five employees, and I work now as Art Director at Ubisoft, one of the biggest development studios in the world. There are 1,300 employees in the same building and still counting. We put out three AAA games a year, with huge structures and pipelines, and short deadlines. But in the end, the work is all about passion."

Future
I think that CG arts fields will continue to grow, and the 2D and 3D mediums will converge more and more. This will happen in all areas of professional creation: concept design; matte painting; architecture; and VFX. More traditional artists will switch to CG. Things are only starting to get interesting.

Steel
3ds max, ZBrush, Photoshop
This was my first attempt at using ZBrush in my work process. I quickly came up with a very nice re-definition of the muscles and general proportion.
Pascal Blanché, Ubisoft, CANADA

[top left]

Recon
3ds max, Photoshop, VRay
Inspired by old 60s Sci-Fi covers and posters. They always try to retell the entire movie in the one image.
Pascal Blanché, Ubisoft, CANADA

[right]

Boulderdash
3ds max, Photoshop, VRay
Revisiting old mythologies is a proven trick to get some new ideas and concepts. Here is my version of the Sisyphus Mythos. The ball is basically a medley of all the technological elements I've been modelling for the last six years.
Pascal Blanché, Ubisoft, CANADA

[above]

Snailmaster
3ds max, Photoshop
Inspired by the works of Arthur Suydam and Sam Keith. I really like the way they both play with human anatomy, and their attachment for surrealistic characters.
Pascal Blanché, Ubisoft, CANADA

[left]

Mermaid
3ds max, Photoshop
It started with a little mind game around the mermaid theme. Maybe my best work so far, you never know when it happens, but suddenly, there is a clear picture in mind and you know that you can make it right.
Pascal Blanché, Ubisoft, CANADA

[top left]

Journey
3ds max, Photoshop
Inspired by the odd, dark universe of Nihei Tsutomu. I like the way he drew his female characters. They look fragile and strong at the same time. Not the usual manga chick.
Pascal Blanché, Ubisoft, CANADA

[above]

Armoredsuit
3ds max, Photoshop
This is another illustration inspired by Sci-Fi covers and manga. I mixed those two main themes, half-rusty and old school, half-technological and sexy. It was really interesting to find a nice balance between the two worlds.
Pascal Blanché, Ubisoft, CANADA

Arcanum XIII
3ds max, Photoshop
An image built around dark ambience. I wanted to create something that inspired fantasy and lost civilisations but without using the usual visuals. Perhaps H.R. Giger's 'Alien' design work was not so far-fetched.
Pascal Blanché, Ubisoft, CANADA

[right]

Master

antasy 2D

Gluba Vander Hon the Giant
Photoshop
Matt Gaser, USA

Mermaid
Photoshop
Deak Ferrand, HatchFX, USA

Excellence
Fantasy 2D

Excellence

Fantasy 2D

Forest Dragon

JOKER

JOKER

J

J

Q

Q

K

K

Sir Wooden Sword
Photoshop
Kerem Beyit, TURKEY [top]

Deity-king Yangjian
Painter
Jiansong Chen, CHINA [above]

Serpent King
Photoshop, Painter
Jason Chan, USA [top]

Her Valentine
Photoshop
Ian Field-Richards, GREAT BRITAIN [above]

Glass Dragon
Painter, Photoshop
Todd Lockwood, USA

江南可采莲
莲叶何田田
鱼戏莲叶间
鱼戏莲叶东
鱼戏莲叶南
鱼戏莲叶西
鱼戏莲叶北
汉 乐府

Dance of the Lotus
Painter, Photoshop
Jian Guo, CHINA
[top]

Bamboo
Photoshop
Cory Strader, USA
[above]

Tears of fairy
Photoshop, Painter
Eric Tranchefeux, FRANCE

The King's Fairy Catcher
Maya, Photoshop
Steven Stahlberg, MALAYSIA

Excellence
Fantasy 3D

Baektokado
Maya, ZBrush, DeepPain
Laurent Pierlot, USA

Toy Fairies
CINEMA 4D, Photoshop
Alexander Hedstrom, GREAT BRITAIN

Excellence
Fantasy 3D

Excellence

Fantasy 3D

Fairy World
3ds max
Olivier Ponsonnet, FRANCE

Elf
SoftimageXSI, Photoshop
Sang Hyun Bang, KOREA

Excellence
Fantasy 3D

Baby
3ds max, VRay, Photoshop
Client: Meyer en Van Schooten
Olivier Campagne, FRANCE

DNA Stair v4.0
VRay, VIZ, Photoshop
Geoffrey Packer, GREAT BRITAIN

Excellence
Architectural 3D

Excellence
Architectural 3D

Apartments on Paseo de Gracia, Barcelona
3ds max, finalRender, Photoshop
Alex Morris, GREAT BRITAIN *[top]*

Quays Point
3ds max, VRay, **Anthony Hartley-Denton**,
GREAT BRITAIN *[above]*

Museum

Chen Qingfeng, CHINA
[top]

Indoor
LightScape
Chen Qingfeng, CHINA
[above]

An Atrium
3ds max, VRay, Photoshop
Xu Zhelong,CHINA

DT lobby
LightScape
Chen Qingfeng, CHINA
[top]

Interieur
3ds max, VRay, Photoshop
Client: Meyer en Van Schooten
Olivier Campagne, FRANCE [above]

Wuxi Natatorium
3ds max, VRay, Photoshop
Xu Zhelong, CHINA

Rebuilding Bank of China
3ds max, VRay, Photoshop
Xu Zhelong, CHINA

Yacht Interior
3ds max, finalRender
Delta Tracing, ITALY

DNA Stair v2.0
VRay, Photoshop, VIZ
Geoffrey Packer, GREAT BRITAIN

Square gallery, Midday
VIZ, Photoshop
Krystian Polak, AUSTRALIA

A Restaurant
3ds max, VRay, Photoshop
Xu Zhelong, CHINA

Master
Character in Repose 2D

Existence
Photoshop
Jose Manuel Fernandez Oli, SPAIN

Bodhisattva
Photoshop, Painter
Jiansong Chen, CHINA

Character in Repose 2D

Rickster
Photoshop
Henning Ludvigsen, NORWAY
[above]

Young Princess
Photoshop
Valentin Fischer, GERMANY
[above]

Unknown Model Study
Painter
Ji Hyun Kim, KOREA
[top]

Self Portrait
Photoshop
David Cathro, GREAT BRITAIN
[above]

Chinese Persons of Ancient Times
Photoshop, Painter
Weng Ziyang, CHINA

Excellence

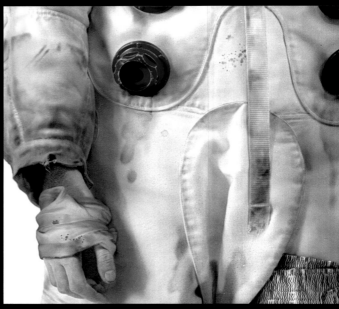

Excellence
Character in Repose 2D

**Your Eyes Would Explode
(If You Had Seen What I Have Seen)**
Photoshop
Jack Youngblood, GREAT BRITAIN

Excellence

Character in Repose 2D

Elanie
Painter, Photoshop
Katarina Sokolova, UKRAINE

Chalk
Painter
Eric Browning, USA

Memories of Hangzhou
Painter, Photoshop
Robert Chang, CHINA

Restrictions
Photoshop, Painter
Jiansong Chen, CHINA
[top]

Freya
Photoshop
Kim Syberg, DENMARK
[above]

Master

Character in Repose 3D

Oriental Heroine
3ds max, Photoshop, Brazil r/s, Client: SONOV
Eun-hee Choi, KOREA

Oriental Hero
3ds max, Photoshop, Brazil r/s, Client: SONOV
Eun-hee Choi, KOREA

Excellence
Character in Repose 3D

Excellence

Steel
3ds max, ZBrush, Photosho
Pascal Blanché CANADA

Armoredsuit
ds max, VRay, Photoshop
Pascal Blanché, CANADA

Excellence

Character in Repose 3D

Crucifixion: Shellshock Nam'67
Maya, Photoshop, Client: Eidos
Xavier Marquis, FRANCE *[top]*

I'm the Evil: Shellshock Nam'67
Maya, Photoshop, Client: Eidos
Xavier Marquis, FRANCE *[above]*

Rescue: Shellshock Nam'67
Maya, Photoshop, Client: Eidos
Xavier Marquis, FRANCE *[top]*

ReVisions
3ds max, Photoshop
Kenn Brown, Chris Wren, CANADA *[above]*

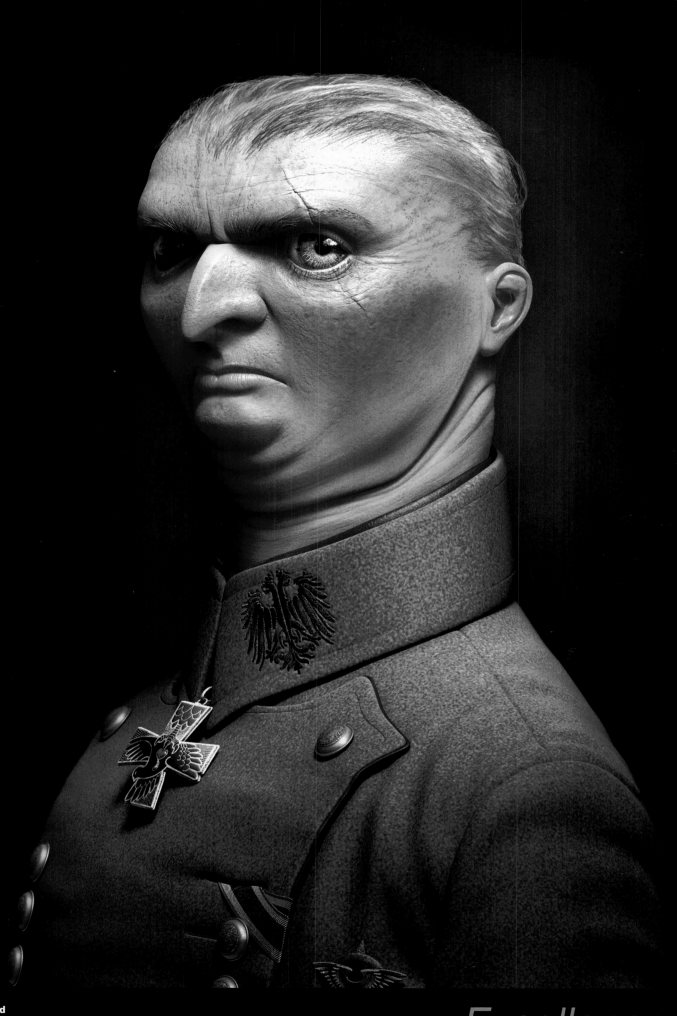

Excellence
Character in Repose 3D

STEPHAN MARTINIERE II⊕⊕III

Master
Character in Action 2D

Monster
Photoshop, Painter
Stephan Martiniere, USA

Excellence
Character in Action 2D

Undead Encounter
Photoshop
Martin Bergstrom, SWEDEN

Springheeled Jack I
Photoshop
Aaron McBride, USA

Excellence
Character in Action 3D

Olympic Runner
Sketchbook Pro
Bobby Chiu, CANADA
[top]

Gathering
Painter
Christian Alzmann, USA
[above]

Knight of fury
Photoshop
Jaime Jones, USA
[above]

Zhai
Painter, Photoshop
Todd Lockwood, USA
[top left]

The Crystal Shard
Painter, Photoshop
Todd Lockwood, USA
[above]

The Grimoire
Photoshop, Painter
Djief, Studio Grafiksismik, CANADA
[top right]

Sons of Grumsh
Painter, Photoshop
Todd Lockwood, USA

Dust empire
Photoshop, Painter
Marc Simonetti, FRANCE

The Baron's flight
Photoshop, Painter
Kornél Ravadits, HUNGARY
top]

On the way II
Photoshop
Xiao Yi, CHINA
[above]

Octopus
LightWave 3D, CINEMA 4D, Photoshop
Leonardo Vilela, Flavio Albino,

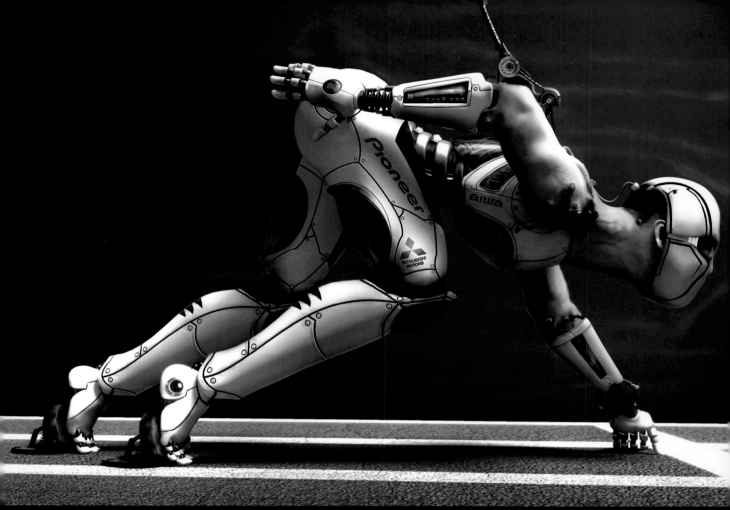

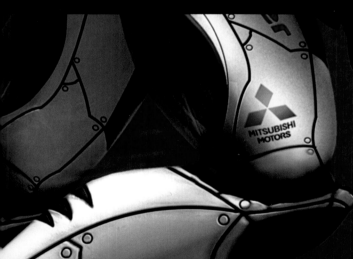

K-Athlete
ds max, finalRender, Photoshop
Carlos Bernardo Delgado Virgen, MEXICO

Excellence

Calite
3ds max, VRay, Photoshop
Renaud de Bellefon, FRANCE

Battlefield: Shellshock Nam'6
Maya, Photoshop
Client: Eidos
Xavier Marquis, FRANCE
[left]

Crab in Living Room
3ds max, Brazil r/s, Photoshop
Fernando Reule,
Seagulls Fly, BRAZIL
[left]

Master
Creature in Repose 2D

Riis, Lost in his Thoughts
Painter
Pierre Droal, FRANCE

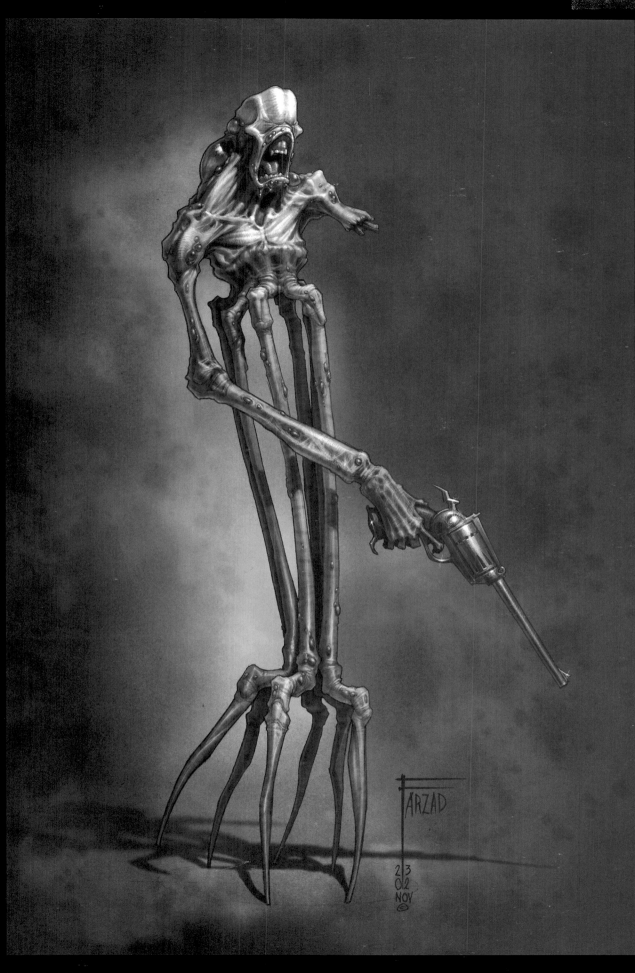

Uncloaked Nightmare
Photoshop
Farzad Varahramyan,
High Moon Studios, USA

Excellence

Creature in Repose 2D

Excellence

Pussy
Photoshop, Painter
Eric Tranchefeux, FRANCE

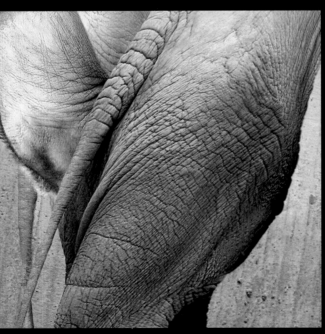

Zoo3000
Photoshop
Alexander Lindt, GERMANY

Excellence
Creature in Repose 2D

King Kong Alone
Photoshop
Alexandre Tuis, FRANCE

Moonlight
Photoshop
Kerem Beyit, TURKEY

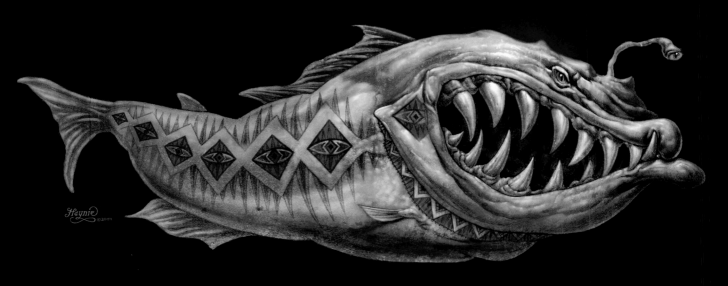

Scary fish
Photoshop
Jeff Haynie, USA
[top]

Bullseye
Photoshop
Jeff Haynie, USA
[above]

Hunter
Photoshop, Painter
Allan Fernando, AUSTRALIA
[above]

Master
Creature in Repose 3D

My Uncle Cthulhu
3ds max, Photoshop, VRay
Fred Bastide, SWITZERLAND

Oddworld Stranger's Wrath: Hero Pose
Photoshop, Maya
CG: Rich McKain, Iain Morton, Character Design: Raymond Swanland
Art Direction: Lorne Lanning **Oddworld Inhabitants**, USA

Excellence

Brachoide
3ds max, Photoshop, HDR Shop
Laurent Gaumer, CANADA [top]

Blue-bee
3ds max
Eugene Rabok, CANADA [above]

The Germ
LightWave 3D, Photoshop
Pete Sussi, USA

Oddworld Stranger's Wrath: Captured By Outlaws
Maya
CG: Rich McKain, Iain Morton, Rajeev Nattam
Character Design: Silvio Aebischer
Art Direction: Lorne Lanning, Gautam Babbar,
Oddworld Inhabitants, USA *[top]*

Oddworld Stranger's Wrath: Ending
Maya, Shake
CG: Rich McKain, Iain Morton Matte Painting: Raymond Swanland
Character Design: Raymond Swanland, Silvio Aebischer
Art Direction: Lorne Lanning, Raymond Swanland,
Oddworld Inhabitants, USA *[above]*

Oddworld Stranger's Wrath: Native Rebels
Maya, Photoshop
CG:Rich McKain, Iain Morton, Character Design: Silvio Aebischer
Art Direction: Lorne Lanning, **Oddworld Inhabitants**, USA

Master

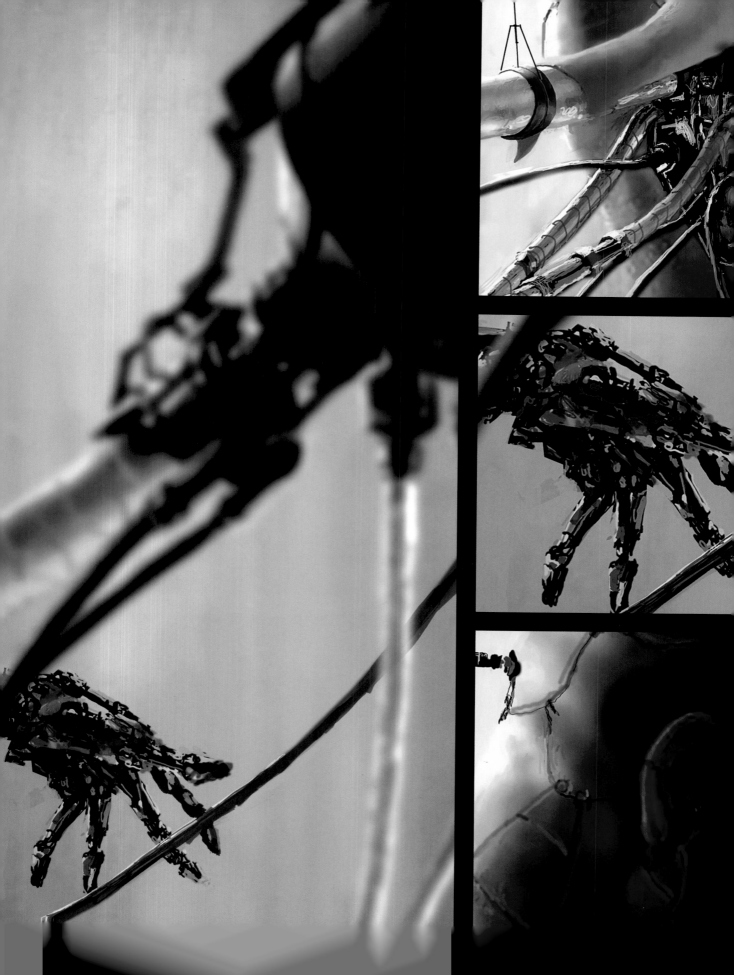

Click Drones
Photoshop
sparth, CANADA

Number Six finds a Friend
Photoshop
Matt Dixon, GREAT BRITAIN
[top left]

Reluctant God
Photoshop
Francis Tsai, USA
[above]

Zonernas Zoologi
Photoshop, Painter
Martin Bergstrom, SWEDEN
[top right]

The Heavy Unit
Photoshop
Mike Hill, GREAT BRITAIN
[top]

Odds
Photoshop
Jiaxing Rong, USA
[above]

Found At Last
Photoshop, Painter
Chris Young, GREAT BRITAIN
[above]

Master
Robotic/Cyborg 3D

The Last of the Leaves
ZBrush, Photoshop
Meats Meier, USA

Xspace
3ds max, Photoshop
Ngo Hock Lim, SINGAPORE

Excellence
Robotic/Cyborg 3D

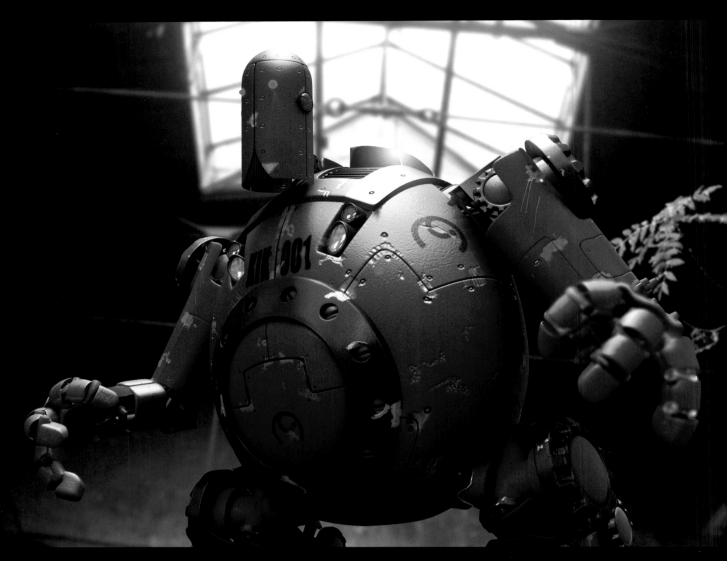

Excellence
Robotic/Cyborg 3D

Robot Carriste
LightWave 3D, Photoshop
Bouchet Christophe, FRANCE

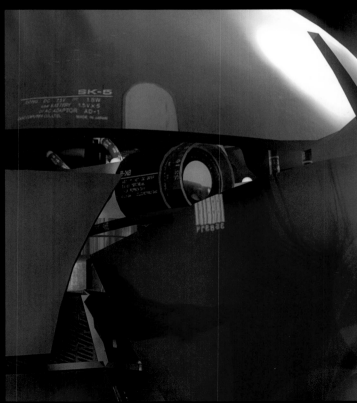

CyberSamurai
3ds max, Photoshop, combustion
Andrea Bertaccini, Tredistudio, ITALY

Excellence
Robotic/Cyborg 3D

Robotic/Cyborg 3D

Tree Frog
Maya, Photoshop

Robot Hopper
3ds max, Photoshop, Brazil r/s

The Household
Photoshop
Cherie Treweek, SOUTH AFRICA

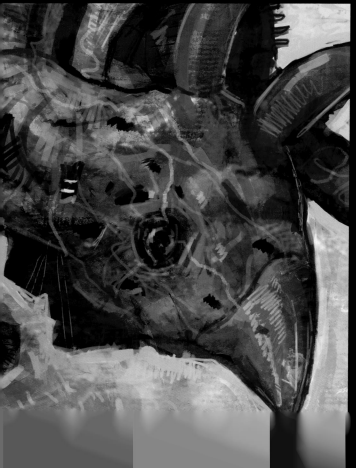
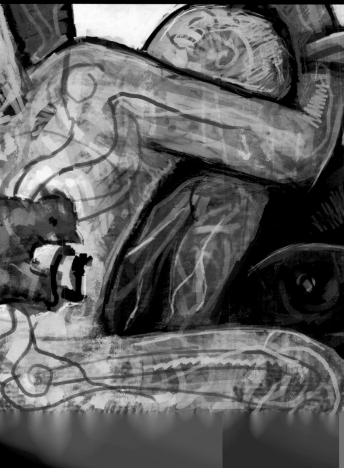

Sequential Escalation
Photoshop
Brandon Williams, USA

Excellence
Abstract & Design 2D

Metamorphosis
Change
Evolve

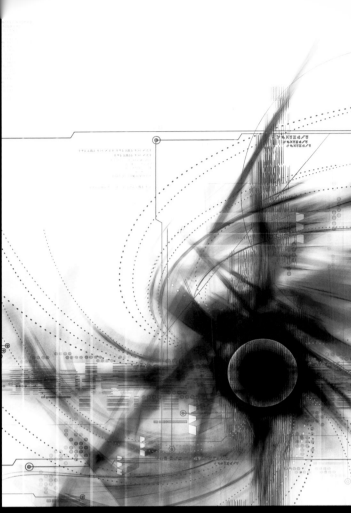

Metamorphosis
Photoshop
Morten Bak, DENMARK [top left]

Confidence
Ultra Fractal
Nicholas Rougeux, USA [above]

The Eye
Photoshop, Illustrator, AfterEffects
Stephany See, Visual Line, MALAYSIA [top right]

Crystal Light
Fractal Explorer, Photoshop
Agnes Dodart, USA

Excellence
Abstract & Design 2D

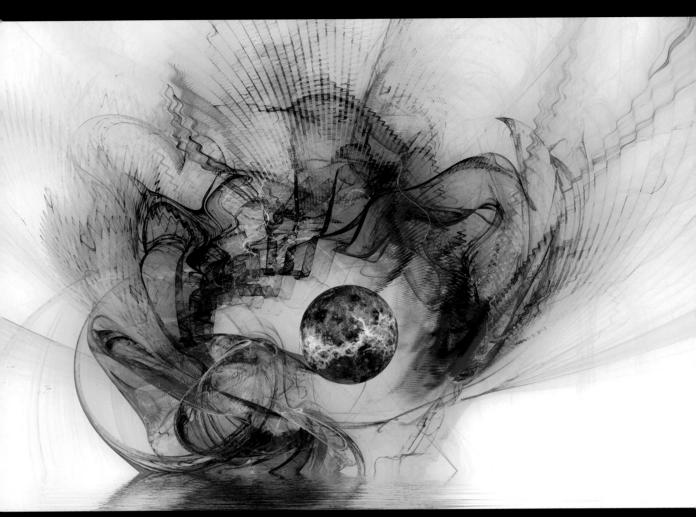

Venustransit
Photoshop
Georg Huebner, AUSTRIA
[above]

Sanctuary
Ultra Fractal
Nicholas Rougeux, USA
[top]

Feelings
Fractal Explorer
Titia van Beugen, NETHERLANDS

Shape.92#2
Photoshop, Realsoft 3D
Tim Borgmann, GERMANY

Shape
Photoshop, Realsoft 3D
Tim Borgmann, GERMANY

Excellence

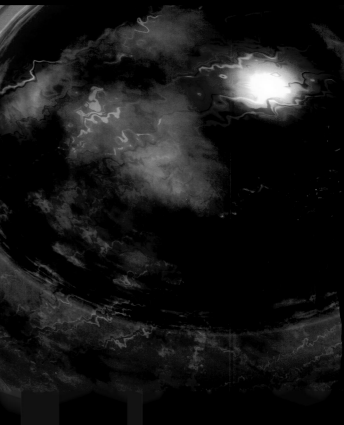

Excellence
Abstract & Design 3D

[GRAFFI-0]

Graffi-D
Photoshop, CINEMA 4D
Tomasz Opasinski, US

Graffi-D
Photoshop, CINEMA 4D
Tomasz Opasinski, US

Alien Heart Surgery
3ds max
John Vega, USA
[top left]

mechONE
Photoshop, Maya
Mikael Lugnegard, SWEDEN
[above]

Shape.60sp
Photoshop, Realsoft 3D
Tim Borgmann, GERMANY
[top right]

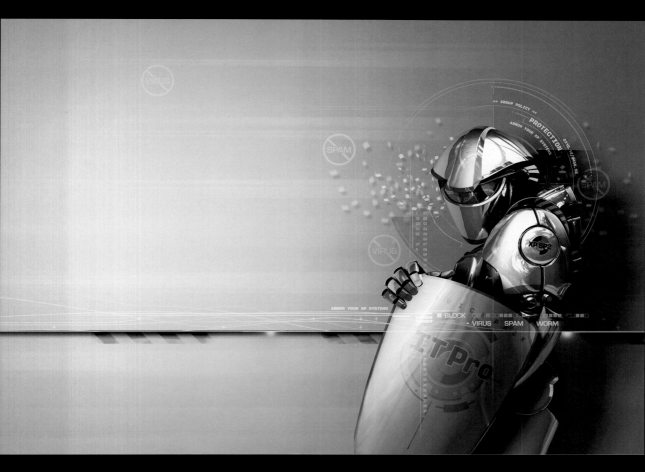

Armor
LightWave 3D, Photoshop, Illustrator
Ryan Etter, USA
[top]

Time
LightWave 3D, Photoshop, Illustrator
Ryan Etter, USA
[above]

Excellence
Humorous 2D

Life is a leaf
Photoshop
Xiao Yi, CHINA

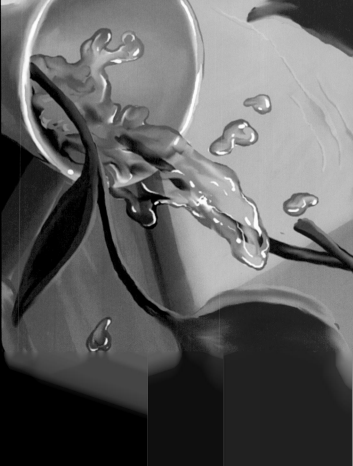

Sir Bunny Vs.
The Wockwurm
Painter
Ursula Vernon, USA
[left]

**Bunnies with
flamethrowers**
Painter
Martin Rebas, SWEDEN
[left]

Bad Egg
Painter
Ursula Vernon, USA

Master
Humorous 3D

Ceremonial Cats II (Cat no. 4)
Maya, Photoshop, Illustrator
Nenad Jalsovec, CROATIA

Excellence

The (last) Flight Of A Mouse
Maya, mental ray, Photoshop
Igor Kudryavtsev, RUSSIA

Automatic Milking Machine
3ds max, VRay, Photoshop
Ila Soleimani, CANADA

Excellence

Humorous 3D

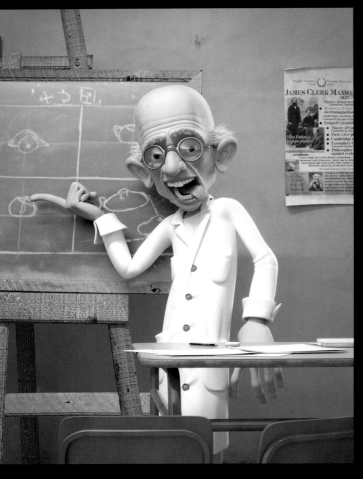

Dr.Maxwell
3ds max
Keytoon Team, SPAIN
[top left]

Dr.Maxwell Posing Test
3ds max
Keytoon Team, SPAIN
[above]

Tiger
Maya, LightWave 3D, Photoshop
Dave Young, USA
[top right]

The Incredible Power of Myopia
3ds max, VRay, Photoshop
Jose M. Andres, SPAIN
[top]

Flying Squirrels
CINEMA 4D
Donald Hanley, USA
[above]

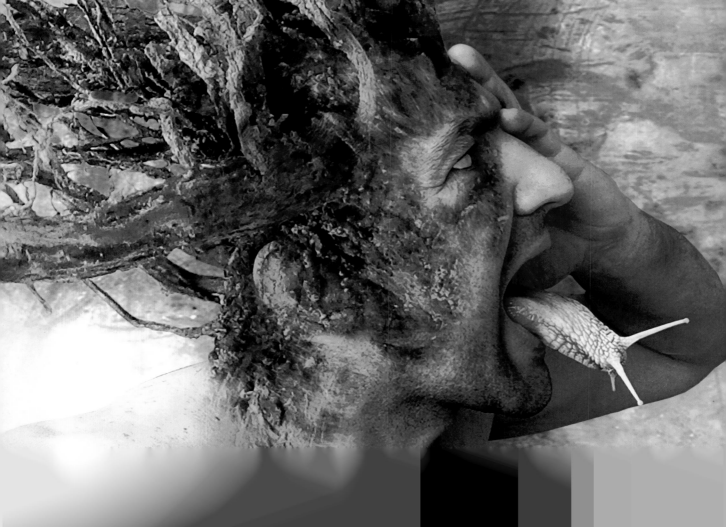

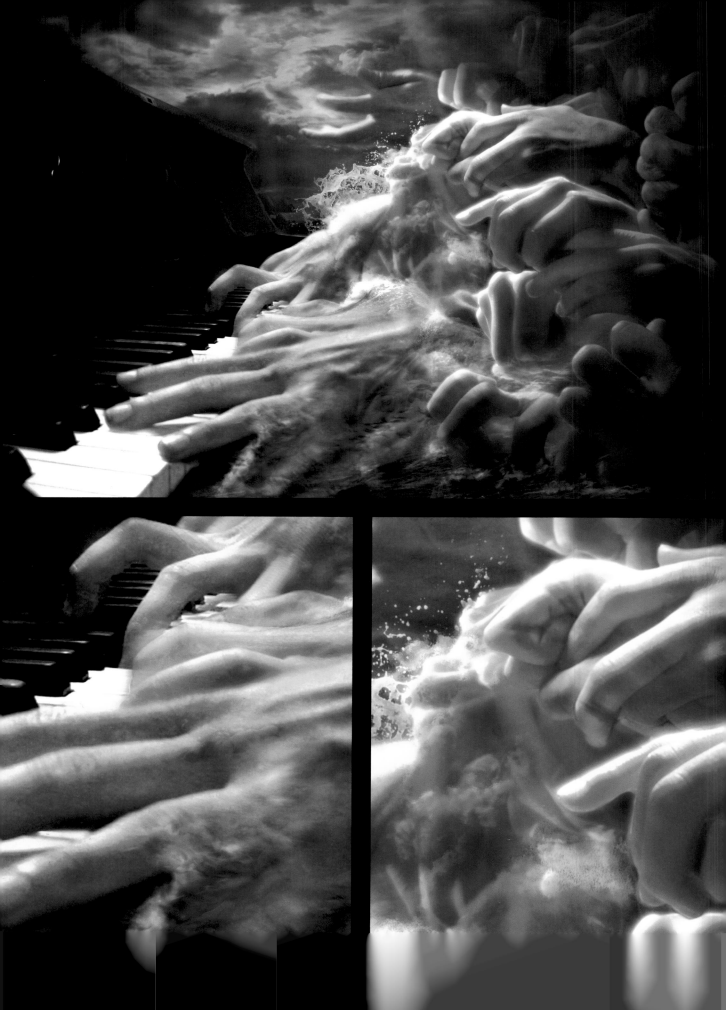

Unfinished but ended
Photoshop
Francesco D'Isa, ITALY

Excellence
Surreal 2D

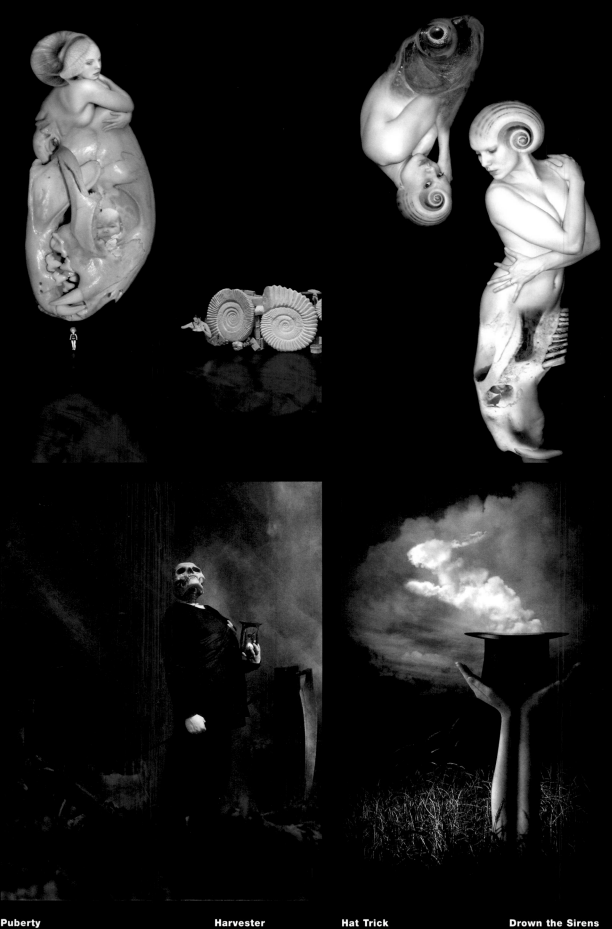

Puberty
Photoshop
Francesco D'Isa, ITALY
[top]

Harvester
Photoshop, Painter
Harri Halme, FINLAND
[above]

Hat Trick
Photoshop, Maya
Felicity Rogers,
NEW ZEALAND [above]

Drown the Sirens
Photoshop
Francesco D'Isa, ITALY
[top]

Infusion
Photoshop
Jason Felix, USA

**Perseus and Andromeda:
A role reversal**
Photoshop
Christina Neofotistou, GREECE
[top]

Atlas
Photoshop
Teodoru Badiu, AUSTRIA
[above]

A Ladder to the Sky
Photoshop
Teodoru Badiu, AUSTRIA
[above]

e Dreamer
otoshop
oderu Radiu AUSTRIA

Crucifixion
Photoshop, Painter
Christina Neofotistou GREECE

Greed
Photoshop
David Gentry GREAT BRITAIN

Escape
Photoshop
Daniele Cascone ITALY

Thallasa
Photoshop, 3ds max
Christos Magganas, GREECE

Excellence

Surreal 3D

Master
Transport 2D

Liquid Car
Photoshop
Nick Pugh, USA

0
Photoshop
Stephan Martiniere, USA

Excellence
Transport 2D

Excellence

Nautilus
Photoshop
Stephan Martiniere USA

Excellence

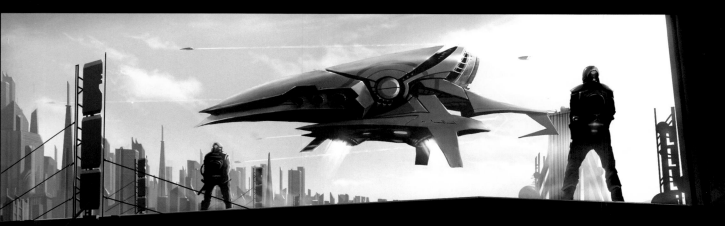

Warship
Photoshop
Thierry Doizon, CANADA
[top]

The landing
Photoshop
Maciej Kuciara, POLAND
[above]

Probability Sun
Photoshop
Stephan Martiniere, USA
[right]

Turtle Travel
Photoshop
Jason Pamment, AUSTRALIA
[top]

The Jump
Photoshop, Painter
Damien Thaller, AUSTRALIA
[above]

Balloon Vessel
Painter, Photoshop
Christopher Davis, GREAT BRITAIN
[right]

Master

Transport 3D

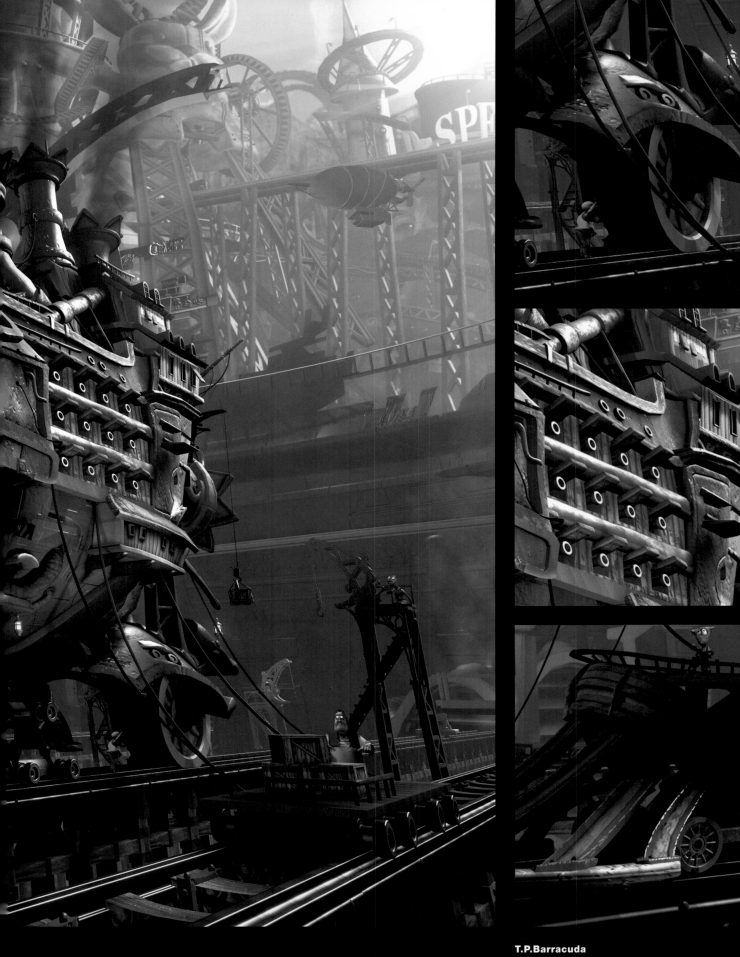

T.P.Barracuda
Maya
Michael Sormann AUSTRIA

Excellence

Marser
3ds max, mental ray, Photoshop
Daniel Trbovic, USA

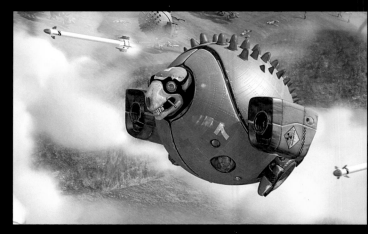

Excellence

Helix Rugens 1
3ds max, Photoshop, VRay
Fred Bastide, SWITZERLAND

The broken armistice over Abalakin
3ds max, Photoshop
Alexander Preuss, GERMANY [top]

Ocean's Satellite
LightWave 3D, Photoshop
Lim Jenn Yu, MALAYSIA [above]

Palm Tungsten | M
LightWave 3D
Riza Endartama, INDONESIA

Master

Environment 2D

The Room
Photoshop
Gary Tonge, GREAT BRITAIN

Old Unused Passage
Photoshop
Ales Horak, CZECH REPUBLIC

Excellence
Environment 2D

Glade
Photoshop, Painter
Chris Beatrice, USA

Master
Environment 3D

Waterfall Castle
Photoshop, SoftimageXSI
Frederic St-Arnaud, CANADA

Mantra
Vue d'Esprit
Thomas Juul Krahn, DENMARK

Excellence
Environment 3D

La Hacienda
3ds max, VRay, Photoshop
Daniel Schmid Leal, MEXICO

Excellence
Environment 3D

wisted Tree
Maya, Photoshop,
enderMan

Sleepy Hollow Western Forests
3ds max
Dijacy Abreu Junior, BRAZIL

The Sunlight of the Purple Vall
3ds max, Photoshop
Wei Weihua, CHINA

Where Fears Roam
Photoshop, Painter, May
Philip Straub, USA

Master
Cityscapes 2D

City Plateaus
Photoshop
Dylan Cole, USA

stephan martiniere 2004

Excellence

I, Robot. Street Down
Photoshop
Stephan Martiniere, USA

Cohabitation
Painter, Photoshop
Philip Straub, USA
[top]

Excellence

A Shadow in Summer
Photoshop
Stephan Martiniere, USA

Avanty World
Photoshop
sparth, CANADA

Excellence
Cityscapes 2D

Dead City
Photoshop
Rowan Cassidy, AUSTRALIA
[left]

Irontown
Photoshop, Painter
Daniel Kvasznicza, AUSTRIA
[above]

Fjord
Photoshop, Painter
Daniel Kvasznicza, AUSTRIA
[top]

Winter-Village
Photoshop, Painter
Daniel Kvasznicza, AUSTRIA
[above]

Master
Cityscapes 3D

Traffic
Bryce, CINEMA 4D, Photoshop
Rudolf Herczog, SWEDEN

Excellence

Fantasy Life
3ds max, Brazil r/s
Jiri Adamec, CZECH REPUBLIC

The Old City Shuyi
3ds max, Photoshop
Wei Weihua, FRANCE *[top]*

Hagia Sophia
LightWave 3D, Photoshop
Juan Jose Gonzalez Diaz, SPAIN *[above]*

焦材油
衣织机地

Excellence
Cityscapes 3D

Memories of my hometown
3ds max, VRay
Wang Ranyun, CHINA

Corner of the Street
3ds max
Jaime Jasso, Metacube, MEXICO

INDEX

EXPOSÉ 3 Limited Edition
The EXPOSÉ 3 Limited Edition features an extra section on the Master Award Winners. These pages can be found in the index with the following reference: *[Limited Edition, i-xv]*

INDEX

The EXPOSÉ 3 Limited Edition features an extra section on the Master Award Winners. These pages can be found in the index with the following reference: *[Limited Edition, i-xv]*

INDEX